Contents

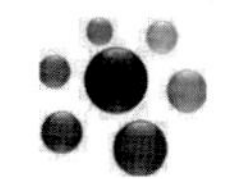

Welcome to your NEBOSH Construction Certificate Revision Guide!

This Revision Guide has been created to help you prepare for your end-of-unit exam for Unit NCC1, and contains important guidance for your Unit NCC2 Construction Health and Safety Practical Application. This Revision Guide is divided into two sections; the first section will help you build a structured revision plan towards your written exam, and at the same time help you develop effective exam technique by providing guidance on how to answer exam-style questions. The second section will guide you through your Unit NCC2 Construction Health and Safety Practical Application, providing you with all the information you need to be fully prepared. We'll focus on the units in order, beginning with NCC1; NCC2 will be covered later in this Revision Guide.

Introduction to Unit NCC1: Managing and Controlling Hazards in Construction Activities

The first section of your Revision Guide will focus on exam revision and strategies for tackling exam questions. It's split into elements as defined by the NEBOSH syllabus and each element-section contains two main parts:

- **Revision Notes**

  When revising for an exam, many students rely on either trying to learn the whole course, which is virtually impossible, or spending most of their revision time on topics they believe are likely to come up in the exam - neither are good revision techniques as they leave too much to chance. This part of your Revision Guide provides a summary of the RRC course material; it's designed to remind you of the key principles and ideas.

- **Exam-Style Questions**

  This part of your Revision Guide provides some example exam questions and model answers. It will give you an insight into what your NEBOSH examiner expects from you and some common mistakes to avoid. These model answers have been written as ideal answers and not under exam conditions or time restraints, so it may not always be possible to write up such a detailed answer in the actual exam. It is also worth keeping in mind that some questions will require you to use knowledge from more than one element of the course.

By combining an overview of each topic with practice exam questions, you're revising the course content and improving your exam technique at the same time - it's perfect preparation for your NEBOSH exam. Remember this booklet has been prepared with the exam in mind - it is **not** intended to replace a proper course of learning!

There's no substitute for hard work, and the more study time you can spare the better, but the key is to use this time effectively.

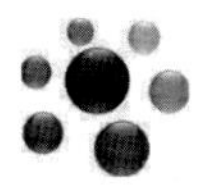

Revising Effectively

Using the Syllabus

Your secret to success is the Guide to the NEBOSH Construction Certificate. This sets out the structure of the course and contains the syllabus. If you don't already have a copy of the syllabus, we strongly recommend that you buy one, keep it with you and read it every day. All NEBOSH exam questions are set from the syllabus, so as you become more familiar with it you'll be less likely to be 'thrown' by a surprise question.

Keep in mind that you'll be expected to apply your knowledge to both familiar and unfamiliar situations!

As exam questions are taken from the syllabus, mapping your study notes against the syllabus can be a very useful revision technique. If you have studied with RRC you will see that the material follows the syllabus quite closely, but this exercise is important to help you appreciate the overall 'picture'. When you're studying one specific section in isolation, it can be very easy to lose sight of how the material fits together, what practical use it is, or how a health and safety practitioner might make use of it in real life. Referring back to the syllabus will put each topic in perspective and help you see how it relates to the field of health and safety generally. It will also help you cross-reference the material with other related topics, which you may have to do in more complex exam questions.

To get this overview, you need to know the elements that make up the course and how they relate to the RRC sections. Each element (e.g. Unit NCC1, Element 1: Construction Law and Management) includes two important sections:

- **Learning Outcomes**, which detail what you should be able to explain, understand, assess, carry out, etc. after completing the element.
- **Content**, which gives you the topics you should be fully familiar with.

You can use both these sections of the syllabus to test whether you have the relevant skills, knowledge and understanding for each element, or whether you need to look again at certain topics.

An idea for an effective revision technique is to take a pin (blunt, of course, for health and safety reasons!) and randomly stick it in any part of the syllabus. Then write down what you know about that topic. This might be very little at first, in which case go back to your study notes and summarise the key issues that you need to work on. Make a note of this topic, then return to it a few weeks later and see how much more you can remember. If you practise this regularly, you will eventually cover the entire syllabus and in the process find that you understand and retain the material much more effectively. This is 'active revision', as it actively tests your memory to see what you have learnt - and it is far more effective than 'passive revision' where you simply read your study notes and usually switch off after 30 seconds, taking in little of the material.

You will find it easier if you make sure that you have an overall understanding of the topic first, then fill in the detailed knowledge requirements later. Ask yourself searching questions on each topic such as:

- 'What use is this?',
- 'How would a health and safety practitioner apply this in real life?',
- 'What is the point of this topic?',

until you feel that you fully understand why a health and safety practitioner would need to know about each area. Once you have this level of general understanding, the details will be much easier to retain, and in some cases you may be able to derive them from your own workplace experiences.

Your revision aim is to achieve this comprehensive overview of the syllabus. Once you have done this, you will be able to at least say something about each of the topic areas and tackle any question set on the syllabus content.

The Exam

The exam for this Unit comprises one long question (worth 20 marks) and ten short questions (worth eight marks each). You have to answer ALL questions.

You have two hours to complete your answers. This means that you have about 25 minutes to answer the long question and around eight minutes for each short question. This should leave enough time for you to read the questions thoroughly before you attempt to answer, and to read through your answers at the end.

NEBOSH are renowned for setting challenging questions and for marking strictly. The examiners are not trying to catch you out, but they do word their questions to ask for specific information. They also expect this information to be given in the requested format.

The most common mistake that students make is not reading the questions properly. Often students provide excellent answers but, unfortunately, they don't answer the question.

Understanding everything in the syllabus is of no use if you have poor examination technique. To achieve maximum marks, you will need to:

- Read the question carefully.
- Understand what information is being requested.
- Understand the breadth of knowledge required.
- Provide the information in a logical and coherent way.
- Manage your time effectively - you need to allocate your time evenly throughout the exam to take into account the number of marks allocated per question.

NEBOSH Command Words

It is important to identify the command word or action verb within the question as this will give you an indication of the depth of knowledge required in your answer. The following meanings of the command words have been identified by NEBOSH.

- **Identify**
- **Outline**
- **Describe**
- **Explain**
- **Give**

Identify

Give the item its name or title, often requiring just a word or short phrase.

Example:

Question: **Identify** FOUR organisational factors that might give rise to a poor health and safety culture within an organisation.

Answer:

- Lack of management commitment.
- Absence of good quality training.
- Lack of consultation on health and safety matters.
- Inadequate resourcing of health and safety management.

Outline

Give a brief summary of the item or its key features. A detailed explanation is not required, but the answers must be more than just a single word or phrase.

Example:

Question: **Outline** TWO categories of worker who might be more vulnerable to risk in a workplace.

Answer:

- Lone workers – workers who work away from immediate and direct contact with their work colleagues.
- Young people – workers who because of their age lack experience in the workplace, are immature and have a poor perception of risk.

Describe

Give a detailed written account of the subject or item. Sufficient so that someone reading that description can visualise the item in their mind's eye.

Example:

Question **Describe** the 'statement of intent' section of a health and safety policy document.

Answer: The statement of intent is usually a one page document with a title at the top of the page followed by several paragraphs of text. At the bottom of the document there will be the name and signature of the person at the top of the organisation (e.g. the Managing Director), along with the date the document was signed and a date when the document will be reviewed. Each paragraph of text on the page will summarise the key aims and objectives of the organisation with regards health and safety.

Explain

Give an understanding of why or how something happens. With more detail than an outline would require.

Example:

Question: **Explain** the moral reason why an organisation should maintain high standards of health and safety.

Answer: The moral reason for maintaining high standards of health and safety arises from the basic human sense of right and wrong. When workers or others are injured or made ill by work activity they will experience pain and suffering. This pain and suffering is morally unacceptable if it can be avoided.

Give

Provide without explanation. Is often used in conjunction with example (as in: 'give an example of').

Example:

Question: **Outline** the meaning of the word 'hazard' and **give** one work-related example.

Answer: The word hazard means 'something with the potential to cause harm'. An example of a work-related hazard would be an electrical flex trailing across the floor of a workroom that presents a risk of tripping.

Exam Strategy

The examination process may seem complex but success is simply a case of averaging around half marks or more for each question. Marks are awarded for giving ideas that are relevant to the requirements of the question, and convincing the examiner that you understand what you're talking about. If you have the knowledge and understanding gained from studying the syllabus as set out above, then this should not be a problem.

Another important exam skill is to carefully read and analyse the question so that you are clear about what is required to answer it. The more you study past exam questions, the more familiar you will become with the way they tend to be phrased and the kind of answer the examiners are looking for.

Students often make the mistake of going into too much detail on specific topics and failing to address the wider issues. If you only deal with half of the relevant issues you can only achieve half of the marks! Try to give as broad an answer as you can, without stepping outside the subject matter of the question altogether. Ensure that you explain each issue to convince the examiner that you have the all-important understanding. Giving relevant workplace examples is a good way of doing this.

Last-Minute Preparation

Finally, a useful way to combine syllabus study with exam practice is to attempt to set and answer your own exam questions. By adding a question word, such as 'explain' or 'describe', in front of the syllabus topic areas you can produce a whole range of questions similar to many of those used in past papers. This is excellent exam practice because it serves as a valuable topic revision aid, and at the same time requiring you to set out your knowledge just as you would under exam conditions.

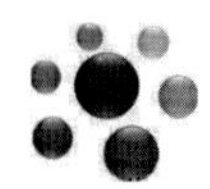

Element 1: Construction Law and Management

Construction work is very varied in nature. Accident statistics show that it is an extremely high-risk activity.

Scope, Definition and Issues Relating to Construction Activities

Types of Work

It includes building works, renovations, alterations, maintenance of existing premises, civil engineering, engineering, decommissioning, demolition and dismantling.

Range of Activities

Construction involves: site clearance; demolition; dismantling; excavation; materials handling; site movements; fabrication; decoration; cleaning; installation, maintenance and removal of services and landscaping.

Particular Construction Issues

There are particular problems which affect construction work, many of which relate to the varied and high-risk nature of the workplace and the type of worker typically involved. They commonly involve transitory sub-contractors with varied levels of skills. Language difficulties may also be a major factor. Clients may also impose time pressures on Principal Contractors which may be passed on to contractors.

Legal, Moral and Financial Consequences of Failing to Manage Construction Health and Safety

Responsibility for health and safety at work rests primarily with the employer. There are moral and financial reasons for employers to be concerned with health and safety:

- Employers provide premises, equipment, and institute working practices. They have a moral responsibility to provide good working conditions.
- Unsafe working conditions have an impact on production and therefore profitability. Negative employer reputation has a damaging effect on public relations and business viability.
- Loss of output causes financial loss. Employers may face fines and/or payment of damages in respect of accidents at work. Insurance premiums are also liable to increase where workplace accidents continue.

Size of the Health and Safety "Problem" in Construction

Introduction of legislation, an extensive publicity programme and advice on accident prevention has produced a consistent reduction in the number of accidents at work. In the UK, there is still an unacceptably high toll in terms of death, injury and financial loss associated with construction incidents.

Scope and Application of the Construction (Design and Management) Regulations (CDM) 2015

The main legal instrument relating to construction is **CDM 2015**, which requires a client to appoint competent persons (duty holders - designers, principal designers, principal contractor and contractors) to plan and carry out construction work that is within the scope of the regulations, each with specific responsibilities and duties (statutory positions) with legal obligations. The regulations also include the requirement for two statutory documents - **the construction phase health and safety plan** and the **health and safety file**.

Duties under the CDM Regulations

Note - be sure to use your course materials to revise the full range of duties for the exam.

- **Clients**
  - Make suitable arrangements for managing a project, including the allocation of sufficient time and other resources.
  - Ensure that these arrangements are maintained and reviewed throughout the project.
  - Provide pre-construction information as soon as is practicable to every designer and contractor appointed to the project.
  - Ensure that before the construction phase begins, a construction phase plan is drawn up by the contractor or the principal contractor.
  - Ensure that the principal designer prepares a health and safety file for the project.
- **Designers**
  - Seek to avoid hazards or minimise risk by effective design.
  - Where risks cannot be avoided, provide adequate information with design drawings and specifications.

- **Principal Designers**
  - Prepare the health and safety file.
  - Plan, manage, monitor and co-ordinate health and safety in the pre-construction phase of a project.
  - Identify, eliminate or control foreseeable risks and ensuring that designers carry out their duties.
  - Prepare and provide relevant information to other duty holders; in particular, principal contractors, to help them plan, manage, monitor and co-ordinate health and safety in the construction phase.
- **Principal Contractors**
  - Plan, manage, monitor and co-ordinate health and safety in the construction phase of a project.
  - Prepare the construction phase plan.
  - Organise co-operation between contractors.
  - Co-ordinate legal requirements for contractor health and safety.
  - Liaise with the principal designer and share information relevant to the planning, management and monitoring of the pre-construction phase, and the co-ordination of health and safety matters, during the pre-construction phase.
  - Ensure that workers are consulted and engaged in securing their health and safety.
- **Contractors**
  - Plan, manage and monitor construction work under their control.
  - Co-ordinate activities with others in the project team.
  - Comply with directions given by the principal designer or principal contractor.
  - Prepare a construction phase plan for single-contractor projects.
  - Ensure that persons they employ:
    - Have the necessary skills, knowledge, training and experience to secure their health and safety.
    - Have appropriate supervision, instructions and information.

Construction Phase Plan

- Sets out the arrangements for securing health and safety during the period construction work is carried out:
  - Site rules
  - Any specific measures for work involving particular risks (Schedule 3 **CDM 2015**).
- Drawn up by the principal contractor (for projects involving more than one contractor) during the pre-construction phase and before the construction site is set up.
- Must take into account the information the principal designer holds (pre-construction information, information obtained from designers) must be reviewed, updated and revised during the construction phase to ensure it remains effective.

Pre-Construction Information

- Provides the health and safety information needed by:
  - Designers and contractors to enable them to carry out their duties.
  - Principal designers and principal contractors to plan manage, monitor and co-ordinate the work of the project.
- Provides a basis for the preparation of the construction phase plan (some material may also be relevant to the preparation of the health and safety file).
- Is information about the project that is already in the client's possession or which is reasonably obtainable by the client, but must:
  - Be relevant to the particular project.
  - Have an appropriate level of detail.
  - Be proportionate to the risks involved.
- Should be gathered and added to as the design process progresses, and reflect new information about the health and safety risks and how they should be managed.

Health and Safety File

- Should include:
  - Drawings.
  - Construction method details.
  - Equipment and maintenance facilities.
  - Maintenance procedures and requirements for the structure.
  - Operation and maintenance manuals and details of utilities.
  - Services, emergency and fire-fighting systems.

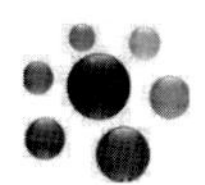

- Responsibility of:
  - Client, to ensure the principal designer prepares the file.
  - Principal designer, to prepare the file in co-operation with the principal contractor.
  - Principal designer, to ensure the file is appropriately updated, reviewed and revised.
  - Principal contractor, to provide principal designer with relevant information for inclusion in the file.
  - Principal designer, to pass the file to the client at the end of the project.
  - Principal designer, to pass the file to the principal contractor if the principal designer's appointment ends before the project finishes.

Duties of Domestic Clients

- People who have building work carried out in their own home that is not business-related.
- Extent to which domestic clients must carry out client duties in **CDM 2015** is limited:
  - Most of the duties are passed to other duty holders.
  - Not required to carry out duties placed on commercial clients, such as managing projects, notification and the general duties in Reg 8.
  - Project involving only one contractor - the contractor carries out the client duties.
  - Project involving more than one contractor - the principal contractor (if appointed) carries out the client duties.

Sources of External Construction Information

Many sources exist, e.g. the Health and Safety Executive (HSE), trade organisations, legislation, etc.

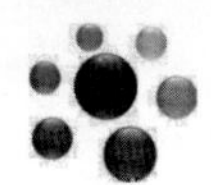

Exam-Style Questions

Short Questions

1. **Identify** the information that should be found in a health and safety file and the construction phase plan as required by the **Construction (Design and Management) Regulations 2015**. (8 marks)

2. **Describe** the main duties of the client of a construction project as set out in the **Construction (Design and Management) Regulations 2015**. (8 marks)

3. (a) **Identify FOUR** duties of the designers of a structure as set out in the **Construction (Design and Management) Regulations 2015**. (4 marks)
   (b) **Explain** how the failures of designers to comply with their duties under these regulations can cause health and safety problems during the construction phase of a project. **Give** practical examples where appropriate to illustrate your answer. (4 marks)

   (Total: 8 marks)

4. A local authority intends to renovate a canal as part of a proposed flood defence system. The local authority plans to select a contractor to drain and clear a section of the canal prior to refurbishment of a culvert.
   (a) Briefly **explain** the responsibilities of the client (the local authority) in making the appointment. (2 marks)
   (b) **Outline** the information that the local authority might request from contractors in order to establish their suitability for the job. (6 marks)

   (Total: 8 marks)

Long Question

5. **Outline** the duties that the following persons have in managing a construction project as set out in the **Construction (Design and Management) Regulations 2015**:
   (a) The client. (5 marks)
   (b) The principal contractor. (5 marks)
   (c) The designer. (5 marks)
   (d) The principal designer. (5 marks)

   (Total: 20 marks)

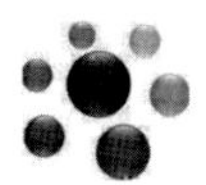

Model Answers

Short Questions

1. **Health and Safety File**

- A brief description of the work carried out.
- Appropriate drawings of structures and layout of services.
- Survey information (e.g. asbestos) and groundwork plans.
- Location of services (water, gas, electricity, etc.).
- Key structural issues and safe loading of floors, roofs, etc.
- Safety information regarding any hazardous substances or materials used.
- Information regarding maintenance issues, e.g. window cleaning.
- Access to plant and equipment and the methods that should be adopted (e.g. safe access onto roofs).
- Manufacturers' instructions and manuals for new equipment included in the project.

Construction Phase Plan

- A description of the project, such as key dates and details of key members of the project team.
- The management of the work, including:
  - The health and safety aims for the project.
  - The site rules.
  - Arrangements to ensure co-operation between project team members and co-ordination of their work, such as regular site meetings.
  - Arrangements for involving workers.
  - Site induction.
  - Welfare facilities.
  - Fire and emergency procedures.
- The control of any particular risks where they are relevant to the work involved.

2. Clients must:

   - Make suitable arrangements for managing a project, including the allocation of sufficient time and other resources.
   - Ensure that these arrangements are maintained and reviewed throughout the project.
   - Provide pre-construction information as soon as is practicable to every designer and contractor appointed to the project.
   - Ensure that, before the construction phase begins, a construction phase plan is drawn up by the contractor or the principal contractor.
   - Ensure that the principal designer prepares a health and safety file for the project.

3. (a) Duties of a designer are to:

   - Ensure the client is aware of their CDM duties.
   - Take into account the general principles of prevention and any pre-construction information to eliminate, reduce or control health and safety risks.
   - Provide information on risks to the principal designer.
   - Ensure appropriate information is included in the health and safety file.
   - Provide, with the design, sufficient information to adequately assist the client, other designers and contractors to comply with their CDM duties.

   (Only four are required.)

   (b) How failures of designers can cause problems during the construction phase:

   - Buildability issues had not been addressed.
   - Risks not addressed at design stage.
   - Insufficient thought given to specifying safer materials.
   - Insufficient information given with the design to enable risk recognition.

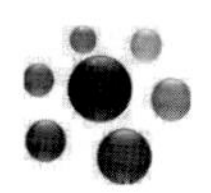

4. (a) In answering this part of the question, it is necessary to have a picture of a canal in mind (rural or urban) and to consider a broad range of issues that might arise from the work.

    While the local authority, as client, has the overall responsibility for appointing the contractor or principal contractor, a responsible person to act as project co-ordinator from within the authority would act in the role of client in making the appointment.

   (b) The information that is required before making the appointment of the contractor:

    - Experience and qualifications of the contractor.
    - Information on the contractor's accident record.
    - Quality of the contractor's safety policy document and method statements.
    - Enforcement record.
    - Outstanding enforcement notices.
    - Training records of employees.
    - Method of selection of sub-contractors.

Long Question

5. (a) The duties of the client are to:
   - Make suitable arrangements for managing a project, including the allocation of sufficient time and other resources.
   - Ensure that these arrangements are maintained and reviewed throughout the project.
   - Provide pre-construction information as soon as is practicable to every designer and contractor appointed to the project.
   - Ensure that, before the construction phase begins, a construction phase plan is drawn up by the contractor or principal contractor.
   - Ensure that the principal designer prepares a health and safety file for the project.

   (b) The duties of the principal contractor are to:
   - Plan, manage, monitor and co-ordinate the health and safety in the construction phase of a project.
   - Prepare the construction phase plan.
   - Organise co-operation between contractors.
   - Co-ordinate legal requirements for contractor health and safety.
   - Liaise with the principal designer and share information relevant to the planning, management and monitoring of the pre-construction phase and the co-ordination of health and safety matters during the pre-construction phase.
   - Ensure that workers are consulted and engaged in securing their health and safety.

   (Only five are required.)

   (c) The duties of the designer are to:
   - Ensure the client is aware of their CDM duties.
   - Take into account the general principles of prevention and any pre-construction information to eliminate, reduce or control health and safety risks.
   - Provide information on risks to the principal designer.
   - Ensure appropriate information is included in the health and safety file.
   - Provide, with the design, sufficient information to adequately assist the client, other designers and contractors to comply with their CDM duties.

(d) The duties of the principal designer are to:

- Prepare the health and safety file.
- Plan, manage, monitor and co-ordinate health and safety in the pre-construction phase of a project.
- Identify, eliminate or control foreseeable risks and ensuring that designers carry out their duties.
- Prepare and provide relevant information to other duty holders; in particular, principal contractors, to help them plan, manage, monitor and co-ordinate health and safety in the construction phase.

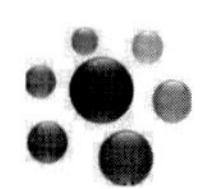

Element 2: Construction Site Hazards and Risk Control

Initial Site Assessment

Before any construction work can begin, a risk assessment must determine what hazards are present and what factors particular to the site may affect risk. For example:

- **Previous/Current Use of Land**

  Building development might take place on rural or green field sites or brown field sites in urban areas. Where a site has been used before, the nature of any existing structures should be established.

- **History of Site**

  The previous use(s) of the site can leave land and buildings contaminated by substances (e.g. asbestos, lead, etc.) that can have both acute and chronic effects.

- **Area of Site: Restrictions**

  It is important to determine whether the construction site has any restrictions placed upon it; e.g. is in an Area of Outstanding Natural Beauty (AONB) or Site of Special Scientific Interest (SSSI). Other restrictions on land for construction could include:

  - National or regional planning authorities placing planning or statutory restrictions.
  - Local authorities having regulations, planning restrictions and building by-laws.
  - Buildings listed for preservation.
  - Government trade and industry regulations requiring permission for industrial development.
  - Rights of way.
  - Rights of support.
  - Rights of light.
  - Tunnels, mine workings, and abandoned, active or proposed mineral rights.
  - Ancient monuments (fortresses, tumuli) and burial grounds.

- **Topography and Ground Conditions**

  Topographical mapping will give a representation of local features on a map and other specialist techniques will help determine the ground characteristics and conditions arising from landfill gas, chemical contamination, water deficiency, settlement and ground instability or extremes of heat.

- **Other Activities on Site**

  It is important to consider the impact that construction work is likely to have on the local people, environment and facilities (i.e. noise, dust, waste, movement of vehicles, overhead working, etc.).

- **Nature of Surroundings**

  New construction works may affect adjacent property or interests so it is important to investigate and consider any likely damage to existing structures and the effects on local properties, infrastructure, waterways and footpaths.

- **Means of Access**

  All vehicular and pedestrian access for construction purposes needs to be controlled and monitored to prevent contamination. Ownership of roads and weight and height limits need to be checked.

- **Presence of Overhead and Buried Services**

  All overhead and underground services need to be located and identified before work commences, e.g. water, gas, electricity, sewers, telephone, communication and TV cables, pipes, etc.

Appropriate General Site Control Measures

Site Planning

Arrangements should be made for **access to the site**, e.g. warning signs at site entrances and elsewhere; provisions of good visibility; easy movement of vehicles and appropriate areas for waste disposal.

- **Roadways** and pedestrian routes should be well signed, maintained and kept in a good condition with pedestrians segregated from site traffic or a one-way system with traffic controls in place. Local authorities should be consulted where controls on public roads are required.

- **Storage** should be well signed, secured and protected and large enough to accommodate any materials left on site. Dangerous or flammable materials and equipment should be stored in separate areas, away from other materials and protected from sources of ignition.

- **Safe loading/unloading** areas are required. A banksman should be used for reversing operations. Access to certain areas may need to be temporarily suspended, or the site perimeter may need to be extended where crane loading or unloading takes place.

- **Site offices** for contractors and staff will normally be temporary and situated close to the main site entrance. Adequate fire and escape provisions must be in place where required and temporary services should be identified and protected.

- **Lighting** along access routes and in areas with scaffolding and skips should be sufficient to enable people to work and move about safely. Some areas may require more specialist local lighting.
- **Signs** should be provided, as indicated by the Health and Safety Plan. Signs should conform to local and European standards and should be reflective or have local lighting.

Site Preparation for Specialist Activities

The ground on the construction site must be able to withstand specialist activities such as lifting, piling and steelwork erection and heavy machinery traffic. Members of the public must be protected from hazards of such activities and account must be taken of any adverse ground conditions which might affect the safety of personnel who are required to work at height.

Site Security and Means of Protecting the Public

The construction site should be surrounded by a secure **perimeter fence/hoarding** or a sound natural boundary; access gates should be secured when the site is unoccupied.

Protection should be provided for **members of the public** (including **children**) who access the site - whether with or without permission. Pedestrian tunnels/walkways with suitable lighting or false ceilings, crash decks or protective sheeting on scaffolding will protect people from falling materials and/or workers. There should be **barriers and signs** to guard excavations and the plant and equipment should be used. Good housekeeping will help to prevent slips, trips and falls.

Other security measures (i.e. removing ladders; immobilising plant and equipment; isolating electrical equipment, and dangerous materials, etc.) and provision of information will help protect them from the hazards and risks. Suitable **safe viewing points** should also be established.

Safe and secure **storage for plant and equipment** should be provided to protect against theft and injury.

Care should be taken to ensure against **environmental dangers** such as mud on public highways and detergent from wheel-washes seeping into a watercourse, river or lake.

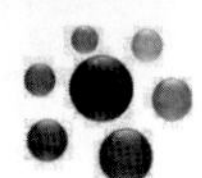

Arrangements with Client/Occupier of Premises

Especially relevant when construction work takes place in or near the client's premises.

During construction work, everyone should be aware of the **site rules** which will include information on:

- Site access.
- Permit-to-work system.
- Required personal protective equipment (e.g. safety footwear, spectacles, hearing protection, hard hats).
- Fire prevention rules (no mobile phones, smoking material, petrol-engined vehicles, etc.).
- Welfare facilities, possibly shared with client, and accessibility.
- Alarms and emergency response.
- First-aid facilities - again, sharing is possible.
- Accident reporting.
- Site transport precautions - speed limits, driver rules, parking, deliveries, loading/unloading.

When working in occupied premises, it is important to have the **co-operation** and **agreement** of others sharing the premises to ensure adequate management of the health and safety risks. This means ensuring the **protection of other employees and visitors** by providing information about the hazards involved and using physical measures. It may even be necessary to evacuate premises being refurbished to ensure that physically impaired or at risk groups are safe.

Where **welfare facilities** and **amenities** are shared on a client site between contractors and workers, these must be of an adequate standard.

Arrangements for Site Inductions

- Principal contractors must provide site inductions and ensure that workers receive training and are competent before starting work.
- Inductions should include: site arrangement details, work conditions, emergency procedures, medical welfare, position of safety equipment, special hazards, permit arrangements, exclusion zones, etc.
- Contractor staff should be told of issues for their specific activity or work area; an informal toolbox talk may be sufficient.
- Training should be reviewed and induction records kept.

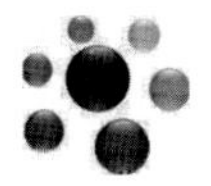

Health, Welfare and Work Environment Requirements

Welfare facilities should be either temporary or fixed, dependent on the duration and nature of the work.

Requirements for **welfare facilities** are laid out in Schedule 2 of the **CDM Regulations**. It includes specifications for sanitary conveniences, washing facilities, drinking water, changing areas and accommodation for clothing, food and drink preparation and eating facilities, ventilation, heating and lighting of facilities and first-aid provision.

Inclement Weather

Working outside can result in exposure to inclement weather. Preventive measures include assessment of weather and rescheduling to avoid bad weather where possible; welfare facilities and shelter; protective clothing, e.g. against wet and cold, sunburn, etc.; safe systems of work; and regular inspection.

Extremes of Temperature

Extremes of temperature can be found indoors and out on construction sites. Thermal comfort is affected by wind speed, ambient temperature, radiant heat and relative humidity.

- Effects of heat include: heat exhaustion/stroke; dehydration; muscle cramps; heat stress; heat stroke; and burns.
- Controls for a hot environment include: limiting exposure time through job rotation and regular breaks; providing cool refuges; providing good ventilation; insulating or shielding of heat sources; and providing access to drinking water and PPE as required.
- Effects for cold include fatigue, slowing of reactions and thinking, loss of dexterity, shivering, numbness, frost-bite, hypothermia.
- Controls for a cold environment include: limiting exposure time through job rotation and regular breaks; protecting against draughts; shielding or lagging cold surfaces; providing warm refuges and warm clothing; ensuring icy floors or roads are gritted/salted/scraped; and providing access to hot drinks and food.

Violence at Work

Work-related violence is any incident in which a person is abused, threatened or assaulted in circumstances relating to their work.

There are certain circumstances where the risk of violence is increased:

- The handling of high-value goods.
- Refusing a service to customers or clients.
- Censuring clients or customers.
- Contact with customers/clients who are under stress.
- Dealing with employees who may be subject to disciplinary measures, or under the influence of alcohol or drugs.
- Working alone or working at night.
- Working in urban areas.

Control measures to protect against violence at work include:

- Identifying any existing problems; through incident investigation reports, interviews with staff, staff surveys, etc.
- Elimination or substitution, e.g. minimisation of cash handling, minimisation of customer frustration, refusing access to potentially violent customers, etc.
- Engineering controls.
- Procedural measures.
- Individual measures.
- Investigation.
- Preventing violence among employees.

Substance Misuse at Work

Drugs, including alcohol and prescription medications, can significantly impair the senses and reaction times resulting in altered behaviour. There are also long-term effects of misuse, including risks to health. Effects on business can include lower production, an increased safety risk, and absenteeism.

Controls to reduce the risk include establishing a clear policy which may restrict access to drugs in the workplace; establish a testing programme; provide rehabilitation and treatment; establish a disciplinary procedure; and provide information, instruction and training to raise awareness.

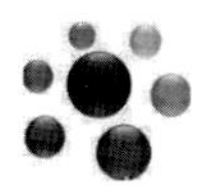

Safe Movement of People on Construction Sites

Hazards to Pedestrians

Pedestrians include people authorised to be walking through a site, e.g. workers, visitors, etc. but will also include members of the general public who walk near a building being built, refurbished or demolished. Children, the elderly and disabled may be at particular risk:

- **Slips, trips and falls** - either on the **same level**, as a consequence of **changing levels**, or from a **height** (which also includes falling into a hole or excavation of some kind).
- **Falls from height** arise from use of steps and stairs, ladders or scaffolding. Hazards: change of level; excavations, manholes, open floor edges; ladders slipping, etc.
- Inappropriate improvisation for access equipment, e.g. use of chairs, boxes, etc.
- **Collisions or striking** - either being hit by something such as a moving vehicle or falling object, or striking a fixed object (including treading on sharp items).
- Injury or damage caused by **environmental conditions** - the effects of noise, heat, dust, sparks or harmful substances in the air.

These hazards may cause immediate injury or longer-term ill health.

Control Measures for Pedestrian Hazards

- A risk assessment will **identify hazards faced by pedestrians** and needs to consider natural movement patterns in and around the workplace, the impact of weather conditions and of maintenance processes as well as the needs of particular groups of people.
- **Floor surfaces** and walkways should be well-built and maintained to cope with traffic levels. There should be adequate **drainage** and **spillages** should be immediately cleaned to guard against slips. Walkways and stairs should be kept as clear of mud and snow as possible.
- There should be sufficient well-defined **traffic routes** and **designated walkways** to allow people to circulate safely and easily. These should be clear of obstructions and equipped with handrails for moderate or steep slopes.
- **Fencing** and **guarding** should be provided on any open walkways where there is a risk of falling or collision with moving vehicles or plant or objects.
- Clearly visible and understood **signs** and warning markings or lights should make pedestrians aware of unfamiliar situations and hazards. Signs should conform with standards specified in the **Health and Safety (Safety Signs and Signals) Regulations 1996** and may indicate prohibitions, warnings, mandatory actions or safe conditions.

- **Personal protective equipment** such as hard hats, anti-slip footwear and dust masks may be necessary for any member of the public entering a particular area where these are worn by workers.
- **Information**, **instruction**, **training** and **supervision** should help ensure that correct procedures are adhered to and that people do not act in an irresponsible manner.

Maintenance of a Safe Workplace

- **Cleaning and housekeeping** to ensure the removal of waste (particularly toxic and flammable waste) and debris.
- Clear passageways and corridors between working areas to ensure safe **access** and **egress**.
- The maintenance of adequate **work environment conditions** (comfortable heating level; adequate lighting to ensure people can see hazards; ear protection or noise protection where noise is unavoidable; use of local exhaust ventilation to reduce or remove risk of dust and fumes).

Protection on Public Highways

Control measures should be taken to protect **members of the public** on a public highway who may be affected by construction activities, including street works. These may include: speed limits, alternative footpaths, suitable guarding/barriers/cones, adequate lighting, flashing warning lights, signage for pedestrians, traffic control, passing points and pedestrian-only zones.

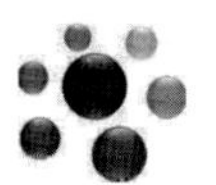

Exam-Style Questions

Short Questions

1. A construction project is going to involve shallow excavations in land previously used as a landfill site.

   Outline the welfare facilities that should be provided for the workers engaged in the project. (8 marks)

2. **Identify** the range of control measures that might be used to minimise the risk of accidents to children who might gain access to a construction site. (8 marks)

3. Extensive scheduled maintenance work is to be carried out by a maintenance contract company, on a piecemeal basis, in a large working warehouse.

   Identify SIXTEEN topic items that should be included in a site induction briefing for the maintenance contractor's employees. (8 marks)

4. **Outline** the requirements relating to sanitary and washing facilities on construction sites as set out in the **Construction (Design and Management) Regulations 2015**. (8 marks)

5. **Outline FOUR** factors that may increase the risk of violence in the workplace. (8 marks)

Long Question

6. A larger water storage tank (4 metres long, 3 metres wide and 2 metres deep) is to be buried in a greenfield site as part of a drainage system.
   (a) **Outline** the main foreseeable hazards that should be taken into account when risk assessing and planning the work. (8 marks)
   (b) **Outline** the key components of a method statement to ensure safety during the excavation and installation work. (12 marks)

   (Total: 20 marks)

Model Answers

Short Questions

1. Welfare facilities to be provided:

    - Hot and cold (or warm) running water with soap and towels available.
    - Showers.
    - A sufficient number of toilets and provision of changing rooms with separate storage for contaminated and clean clothing.
    - Facilities for clothes drying.
    - A separate room for eating meals and refreshments with means to boil water and heat food.
    - Adequate first-aid facilities and a trained first aider.

2. Ways of minimising accidents to children:

    - Preventive measures:
        - Provision of secure hoardings and fences to prevent access.
        - Warning signs of dangers (and possibly use of security patrols).
    - Should access be gained:
        - Removal of access ladders, provide trench supports, cover holes, immobilise plant, isolate electrical supplies, reduce height of stacked materials, lock equipment and chemicals away, secure storage tanks.
    - Local publicity campaign and educational visits to schools to warn of dangers.

    (Eight ways should be given.)

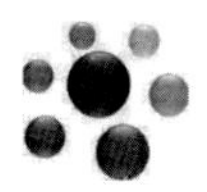

3. It is important that maintenance workers understand site problems and know the safe working practices. Site induction is an important opportunity to get this information across. Items that should be covered include topics such as:

   - Methods and sequence of work.
   - Particular risks in the warehouse (such as movement of FLTs).
   - Access and egress to the site and traffic routes.
   - Prohibited activities.
   - Site rules (including those relating to the wearing of PPE).
   - Procedures for reporting accidents, incidents and unsafe conditions.
   - First-aid and welfare arrangements.
   - Procedures to be followed in the event of an emergency.

4. The requirements of **CDM 2015** with respect to sanitary and washing facilities are:

   - Where practicable, flush toilets should be provided with separate facilities for men and women, unless they are in a room intended for one person and door may be locked from inside.
   - Washing facilities should include a supply of hot and cold (or warm) running water, soap or other cleansing agent.
   - Means of drying clothing.
   - If the nature of the work demands, showers should be provided.
   - Sanitary and washing facilities should be adequately lit and ventilated, kept in a clean condition, sufficient in number for the employees on site.

5. The risk of violence in the workplace may be increased by:

   - The handling of cash.
   - Contact with the public/customers where a request may be refused.
   - Contact with an authority figure, e.g. a traffic warden.
   - Contact with customers/clients under the influence of drink or drugs.

Long Question

6. (a) In asking for an outline, the examiners would expect hazards to be identified as well as the associated risks being further detailed.

   - Ground conditions, the type of ground and possibility of contaminants.
   - Excavation work with the risk of collapse of sides and possibility of people or vehicles falling into the excavation.
   - Groundwater and risk of flooding and leptospirosis from rats.
   - Lowering of the tank into the excavation with risk of crane overturning if not correctly rated for the job.
   - Presence of services (underground or overhead services) with associated risk of electrocution

   (Eight items are required.)

   (b) The key components included in a method statement would be:

   - Duration of the work.
   - The number of personnel involved.
   - Competency of personnel.
   - Means of site access and egress.
   - Identification of machinery and plant involved.
   - Arrangements for inspection and maintenance of machinery.
   - Means of support and edge protection for the excavation.
   - Positioning of spoil.
   - Arrangements for dealing with overhead and underground services.
   - PPE.
   - Welfare arrangements.
   - Procedures to be followed in the event of fire.

   (Twelve items are required.)

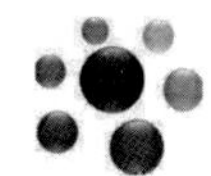

Element 3: Vehicle and Plant Movement - Hazards and Risk Control

Safe Movement of Vehicles and Plant within a Construction Environment

Hazards from Workplace Vehicles and Plant

- **Loss of control** - where the vehicle is not under the full control of the driver, due to **mechanical failure** and **environmental conditions**.
- **Overturning** - tipping over onto the vehicle's side or onto its front or back. Instability, particularly of high-sided vehicles, may be due to speed of travel, steepness of slope, height and stability of the load, tyre pressure and road conditions.
- **Collisions with other vehicles, pedestrians or fixed objects** due to driver incompetence; adverse ground and weather conditions; poor lighting or site layout; congestion.
- **Site layout** - the layout of construction sites should be well planned and organised with appropriate areas for vehicle manoeuvres; well established and defined traffic routes, with passing and reversing points and physical protection for pedestrians; properly signed and marked loading and refuelling areas and access for emergency services.

  Road surfaces should be suitably firm and maintained in good condition to prevent accidents and damage to the vehicles themselves.
- **Gradients** - great care should be exercised to ensure that vehicles are designed and selected to operate on gradients/slopes or adverse cambers or where chicanes are in use.
- **Excavations** - the **CDM Regulations** (Part 4) require that adequate measures be taken to ensure vehicles do not fall or overturn when near excavations, pits, or water embankments, such as the provision of banksmen.
- **Scaffolding** - vehicles should not be parked near scaffolding to prevent any materials falling on them.
- **Falsework** - these temporary structures used to support a permanent structure during its erection must be stable (**CDM Regulations**). Vehicle operations near such structures should be minimal particularly in adverse weather conditions.

- **Non-movement related hazards**, including:
  - **Loading/unloading** - falls of people or materials.
  - **Securing/sheeting loads**.
  - **Coupling** - e.g. trailers.
  - **Vehicle maintenance work** - mechanical hazards, working underneath.
  - **Refuelling** - off-site should be encouraged but where on-site refuelling is necessary, fuel should be restricted to diesel or LPG and storage facilities should be away from ignition or heat sources.

Control Measures to Reduce the Risk from Movement of Vehicles and Plant

When assessing risk from movement of vehicles and plant, the following factors should be considered: patterns and volume of traffic, types of vehicle, operations undertaken, segregation required, weather conditions and the local conditions, e.g. lighting, surfaces, etc.

Suitability and Sufficiency of Traffic Routes

All vehicle routes should be clearly marked and separate pedestrians from moving vehicles. The size and layout of routes will be determined by traffic volume and forms of movement required, e.g. reversing, passing, etc. Traffic routes should be suitable for the largest vehicle likely to use them.

Management of Vehicle Movements

The way in which vehicles move around a site should be carefully controlled and be appropriate for the types of vehicle operating on the site. Reversing should be kept to a minimum and speed limits and use of warning systems should be enforced to take account of environmental hazards and presence of pedestrians. There should be sufficient and suitable parking for all vehicles, and signs and markings should be in place to regulate vehicle manoeuvres. Signalling should be used where vehicles need to reverse or manoeuvre and loading and unloading procedures should be observed.

Environmental Considerations

- **Visibility** and **lighting**, particularly where pedestrians or mobile plant are involved or conditions are not clear.
- **Gradient** and **changes of level** will call for safe driving practices particularly where loads are involved.
- **Surface conditions** should be suitable and well drained.

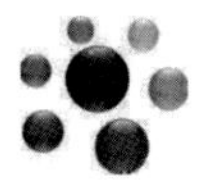

Suitability and Maintenance of Vehicles

An assessment should be carried out regarding the suitability of vehicles on construction sites.

Vehicles on construction sites should be inspected and maintained regularly particularly:

- Braking systems.
- Steering mechanisms.
- Tyres.
- Exhaust systems.
- Audible warning systems that operate automatically when reversing.
- Driving lights, including flashing light warnings.
- Rear view mirrors and/or convex mirrors to overcome blind spots.
- Roll-over and falling object protection.
- Weather-proof cabins.
- Seat belts and restraining systems.
- Fire-fighting equipment.

Requirements for Vehicle/Driver Protection

- Driver protection (Roll-Over Protection Structures (ROPS) and Falling Object Protective Structures (FOPS)) and use of restraint systems.
- Trucks used in demolition should be protected from falling objects or materials and/or suitable head protection should be worn by drivers.
- PPE and weather protection should be provided as appropriate, and vehicles should have suitable foot-steps and handholds to prevent falls when getting in and out of vehicles.

Means of Segregating Pedestrians and Vehicles

These will include:

- Barriers or clear surface markings.
- Designated crossing points.
- Separate access for pedestrians and vehicles where passage is limited.
- Use of high-visibility jackets for pedestrians and warning lights/alarms for vehicles where segregation is not possible.
- Use of additional lighting or mirrors to increase visibility.

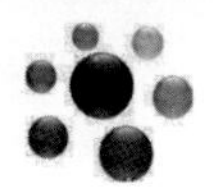

Wherever possible, pedestrians should be physically segregated from vehicle traffic routes.

Protective Measures for People and Structures

- **Barriers:**
  - Vulnerable plant and equipment should be located away from roads or protected by suitably constructed barriers.
  - Padding should be used on columns and pillars to limit collision damage and barriers will separate pedestrians from traffic routes.
  - Traffic routes should have adequate markings, signs and warning signals to inform pedestrians of vehicular movements.
- **Signs, markings and warning signals** can be used to provide information to pedestrians and drivers relating to hazards and site rules.

Site Rules

All drivers using a site should be aware of the rules that apply - directional systems, speed limits, parking, etc. Visiting drivers should be made aware of rules on entering site.

Special rules will apply to forklift trucks and due attention should be paid to parking, access and egress, and unloading and loading areas.

Selection and Training of Drivers

Drivers must be 17 years old (21 for large heavy goods vehicles), having passed the necessary test(s). Operators should be reliable, able to do the job in a responsible manner, and have a reasonable level of physical and mental fitness and intelligence.

Operator training should include general basic training and specific job training. Refresher training is also beneficial for all drivers.

Assuring Driver Competence

There are three bodies which operate accredited training to prescribed standards to ensure safe operations:

- The Construction Industry Training Board.
- The Agricultural Training Board.
- The Road Transport Industry Training Board (RTITB).

Employers should hold records of all training undertaken by drivers, including that certified by recognised bodies.

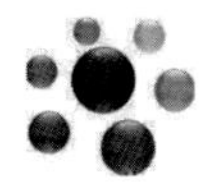

Driving at Work

The risk of fatal or serious injury to persons driving on public roads is several times higher than for people at work.

Factors that Increase the Risk of Work-Related Road Incidents

A policy and risk assessment is needed for work-related road safety. Factors that increase the risk of an incident involving a competent driver include:

- Distance.
- Traffic and driving hours.
- Work schedules.
- Weather conditions.
- Stress or fatigue.

Managing Work-Related Road Safety

Employers are responsible for managing work-related road risk. Factors to consider include:

- Provision of a Safe Driving policy.
- Systems to manage work-related road safety.
- Monitoring road safety performance.
- Organisation and structure - to allow co-operation between departments.
- Legal responsibilities of individuals on the public highways.

Risk Assessment of Road Risk

When carrying out an assessment on work-related road risk, consideration should be given to factors relating to the driver, vehicle and journey.

- Driver - competence; required licence(s); experience; training; general fitness and health.
- Vehicle - suitability for task and driver; condition; including safety equipment and protection systems; vehicle-specific training; and ergonomic issues.
- Journey - route planning including suitability for vehicle, size restrictions, and hazards present; realistic schedules taking account of traffic flow and time required to complete journey safely; potential to reduce journey, perhaps through use of different mode of transport; and consideration of adverse weather disrupting journey.

Control Measures to Reduce Work-Related Driving Risk

General control measures relating to appropriate policies and management of risk should be in place, but the most effective control will always be **elimination**.

If elimination is not possible, then consider alternative transport; vehicle sharing; planning routes and schedules realistically; planning journey distance and times; scheduling stops as required; ensuring vehicle maintenance is carried out; ensuring driver competence, fitness and health; monitoring performance, etc.

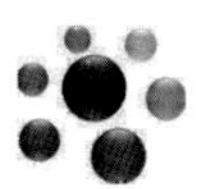

Exam-Style Questions

Short Questions

1. **Outline** the primary hazards associated with the movement of people and vehicles. (8 marks)

2. **Outline** a control strategy to prevent pedestrians and vehicles coming into contact with each other. (8 marks)

3. **Identify FOUR** factors to be taken into consideration when selecting potential drivers for workplace transport and equipment. (8 marks)

4. **Describe FOUR** conditions that may cause a forklift truck to overturn in the workplace. (8 marks)

Long Question

5. Many fatal accidents involve workers being struck by vehicles.

   Outline the range of precautions that can be introduced in a workplace to reduce risks of vehicle accidents. (20 marks)

Model Answers

Short Questions

1. The primary hazards associated with the movement of people and vehicles are:
   - Slips, trips and falls on the same level and from height.
   - Collision with moving vehicles.
   - Collision with or being struck by a falling object, e.g. part of a load.
   - Striking against fixed or stationary objects.
   - Environmental conditions.

2. To prevent pedestrians and vehicles coming into contact with each other, the following control strategy should be applied:
   - Segregation.
   - Pedestrian routes and vehicle routes.
   - Speed limits.
   - Signage; audio and/or visual alarms.
   - Road marking.
   - Training of drivers.
   - Guarding and barriers.
   - Maintenance of floor and traffic routes.
   - Employee awareness.

3. When selecting potential drivers for workplace transport and equipment, the following factors should be taken into consideration:
   - Competence.
   - Training in use of any special features or requirements.
   - Age - generally at least 17 years old.
   - Reliability.
   - Able to perform task in a responsible manner.
   - Reasonable fitness.
   - Reasonable intelligence.

   (Only four factors are required.)

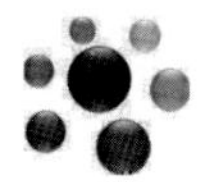

4. A forklift truck may overturn due to:
   - Loss of control.
   - Speed of travel.
   - Steepness of a slope.
   - Travelling with a raised load.
   - Uneven tyre pressure.
   - Poorly-maintained road surfaces.
   - Environmental conditions.
   - Wind.

   (Only four reasons are required.)

Long Question

5. A strategy to reduce the risk of vehicle accidents will include the following precautions:
   - Road systems clearly lit and one-way traffic clearly marked.
   - Space for parking, reversing, loading and unloading.
   - Use of crossings and white and yellow lines.
   - Vehicles not allowed to reverse unless necessary and then only with a banksman and controls, like alarms.
   - Avoiding sharp bends.
   - Protection of vulnerable plant.
   - Barriers.
   - Segregation of pedestrians and vehicles.
   - Parking areas.
   - Maintenance of roadways.
   - Speed limits and restrictors.
   - Signage.

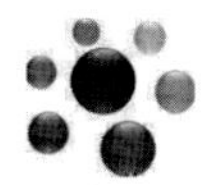

Element 4: Musculoskeletal Hazards and Risk Control

Musculoskeletal Disorders and Work-Related Upper Limb Disorders

- **Musculoskeletal disorders (MSDs)** includes all disorders that affect the body's muscles, ligaments, tendons, joints, nerves and other soft tissues. Included are upper-limb disorders.
- **Work-Related Upper Limb Disorders (WRULDs)** are injuries occurring in the upper body (the hands, arms, wrists, fingers, neck and shoulders) usually affecting the soft tissue, and caused or contributed to by a worker's activities in the workplace.

Examples in Construction

Repetitive construction activities that can cause MSDs and WRULDs include digging, kerb laying, fixing plasterboard, laying bricks and concrete slabs, scaffold erection/ dismantling, and use of DSE.

Ill-Health Effects of Poorly Designed Tasks or Workstations

Physical stress and **muscular problems**, because of poor posture or repetitive action, may include:

- **Work-related upper limb disorders**, such as tendonitis, tenosynovitis, ulnar neuritis, carpal tunnel syndrome and thoracic outlet syndrome.
- **Back disorders**, including slipped discs, aches and pains.
- **Eye strain** and other visual conditions (i.e. blurred vision) due to excessive brightness or flickering or prolonged concentration on displayed information.
- **Mental stress** caused by excessive or conflicting demands.

Factors Contributing to Ill Health

These can be divided into:

- The **task** - physical requirements, e.g. posture and physical action, forces involved, repetition, duration and recovery time.
- The **environment** - particularly lighting, e.g. illumination, contrast, glare. Cold or damp conditions should also be considered.
- The **equipment** - physical characteristics of the equipment and position in relation to user. Also consider worker interaction with the work equipment itself - can it be adjusted?

Appropriate Control Measures

Ergonomics is the study of the relationship between the worker, the work that they are doing, and the environment in which they are doing it.

The objective is to match the workplace to the individual needs of the workers. Work tasks and layout should be adapted to suit the individual and reduce the potential for injury or error.

Manual Handling Hazards and Control Measures

Common injuries caused by manual handling are:

- Back injuries - MSDs - caused by twisting, lifting or pushing loads.
- Muscular problems - strains and sprains.
- Hernias - rupture of the musculature of the body cavity wall.
- Cuts, abrasions and bruising.
- Bone injuries - cracks and fractures.
- WRULDs - these affect the soft tissues of the wrist, neck, shoulders and arms.
- Exposure to hazardous substances.

Assessment of Manual Handling Risks

The **Manual Handling Operations Regulations 1992, as amended**, identify four factors to be considered in a risk assessment of manual handling operations; the **t**ask, **i**ndividual, **l**oad and **e**nvironment (TILE):

- The **task** - the nature of the handling operation and identification of high-risk activities.
- **Individual capability** - the physical characteristics of the persons doing the handling operation and their ability in terms of knowledge and skills.
- The **load** - including measurements of the object(s) being handled.
- The **working environment** - the immediate physical surroundings within which the handling operation takes place (i.e. are the floors in good condition? Is lighting good enough? Is movement restricted?).

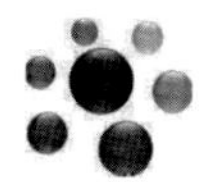

Minimising Manual Handling Risks

Task

The design of the task should be considered, including consideration of:

- Sequencing.
- Work routine.
- Using teams.
- Mechanising or automating tasks.

Individual

Employees expected to carry out manual handling tasks must have adequate training, instruction, information and supervision. Individuals with health problems should be considered and health monitoring and reporting systems must be in place.

- Employees should understand the importance of:
  - Design of tasks, including workplace layout.
  - Recognising different types of loads and assessing the weight and balance of loads to deciding which loads can be handled alone and which should be team-handled.
  - Safe lifting and handling techniques.
  - Correct use of PPE.
  - Correct use of mechanical aids.
- Design characteristics of handling tasks and use of mechanical equipment can greatly improve manual handling on construction sites.

Load

When assessing a load, the following aspects should be considered:

- Weight and size.
- Making the load easier to grasp.
- Making the load more stable and rigid.
- Making the load less damaging to hold.
- Markings.

Working Environment

The conditions in which the manual handling is carried out should be assessed, with consideration given to:

- Workplace design.
- Floor conditions.

- Changes of level.
- Atmospheric conditions.
- Personal Protective Equipment (PPE).

Efficient Movement Principles for Manual Lifting

Efficient movement principles should be applied when lifting loads. They are designed to avoid WRULDs due to lifting and putting down loads, poor posture and repetitive or awkward movements. The principles consider the lifting activity in three stages - **preparation**, **lifting** and **setting down**.

Lifting and Moving Equipment

Lifting and moving devices fall into two categories:

- **Mechanically-operated load moving equipment** - e.g. forklift trucks (including rough-terrain trucks); telehandlers; dumper trucks; excavators; lifts and hoists; conveyors; and mobile and tower cranes.
- **Manually-operated load-moving equipment** - e.g. wheelbarrows, sack trucks and pallet trucks.

Each type of equipment will present its own hazards (see table) but there are some general hazards associated with mechanical lifting devices:

- Mechanical failure.
- Overloading.
- Collision with pedestrians, other vehicles or structures.
- Falls of materials or persons.
- Noise.
- Contact with moving parts or crushing hazards.
- Smoke, dust, fumes from the exhaust gases.
- Fire and/or explosion when refuelling.

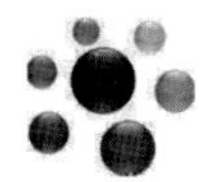

Device	Hazards	Control Measures
Forklift trucks	Lack of maintenance or driver training. Unstable loads or driving with raised loads.	Operator training and use of seat belts. Daily checks and maintenance by a competent person. Rollover protection.
Telehandlers; excavators	Impact with people, materials, scaffolding or structures. Falling into trenches or holes in the ground.	Safe Working Load (SWL) marked, correctly designed and manufactured lifting point and fitting of outriggers (stabilisers) with interlocking devices.
Dumper trucks	Crushing hazards. Smoke, dust, fumes from the exhaust gases or fire when refuelling.	Restraint systems to be fitted; competence training of operator and adequate maintenance of machine.
Lifts and hoists	Fall from height or collision with hoist or lift.	Regular inspection and testing by competent person. Safe working loads. Use of barriers and cages to prevent falls.
Conveyors (belt, roller and screw)	Trapping points at in-running nips. Entanglement and contact with moving parts such as in screw conveyors. The falling of materials from conveyors.	Use of guards and use of trip wire where appropriate.
Mobile and tower cranes	Uneven ground and high winds causing crane to topple. Jib (arm) or load striking something whilst moving. Driving with a suspended load.	Use of correct crane; trained and competent operators. Regular inspection and maintenance by a competent person. Use of fail-safe devices.
Manually operated load moving equipment	Overloading or loading incorrectly can cause trucks to topple. Equipment can also run away on slopes. Careless parking can obstruct and cause trips/falls.	Consider route to be used and provision of ramps. Load should be appropriate to type of truck used. Regular inspection and maintenance. Use of PPE for operators if appropriate.

Accessories for Lifting Operations

A range of different accessories may be used in lifting operations, including: chains; 2, 3 or 4-legged slings; endless slings; webbing straps (or strops); fibre ropes; shackles; eyebolts; lifting beams; and hooks.

Other types of lifting tackle are available, but they all work along the same principle acting as a suitable **connection between the load and the crane**.

Control Measures for Lifting and Moving Equipment Operations

Safe Systems of Work (SSWs)

SSWs are required for all forms of mechanical handling equipment.

The **handling equipment** should be appropriate for the task, be in good condition, made from sound materials, of adequate strength and free from faults.

The **load** should be packed in a manner to minimise the risk of handling accidents; and be of a suitable size/weight for the handling equipment, items stable within a rigid container and appropriate load information given.

The **working environment** must be designed in such a way as to ensure the safe operation of the equipment at all times.

Operators should be competent in use of the equipment.

Control Measures for Specific Equipment

- **Forklift Trucks (FLTs)**

  Specific considerations apply to forklift trucks:

  - Operator training is essential. Strict rules about driving exist.
  - Care must be taken in the vicinity of pedestrians, both during movement and when lifting.
  - Before lifting, the load weight must be assessed to ensure that the truck is capable of lifting it.
  - For lifting or lowering loads, the handbrake should be on and the truck left in neutral.
  - Ignition keys must not be left in static trucks.
  - Passengers should not be carried on trucks without suitable platforms.
  - A truck should not be left on a gradient.
  - Tandem lifts or operations should be supervised by a competent person.
  - FLTs must be used and maintained properly in accordance with the manufacturer's specifications.

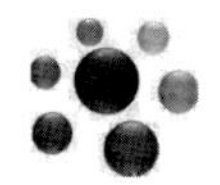

Daily safety checks should be carried out to include:

- Tyre pressures, tyre damage.
- Parking brake, service brakes, and steering gear function.
- Fuel, water and oil in diesel/petrol powered FLTs.
- Batteries of battery-operated FLTs.
- Lifting, tilting and manipulation systems (including attachments) should be working properly.
- Hydraulic systems should be free from leaks, and hydraulic fluid levels correct.
- Audible warning signal; lights; mirrors.
- ROPS where fitted.

■ **Rough Terrain Forklifts and Telehandlers**

Specific competencies of operators are required.

Rough terrain machines require safety devices:

- To prevent lifting a weight beyond the recommended rating.
- To prevent lifting beyond a given height.
- A levelling indicator showing danger zones where raising the load is not allowed.

Telescopic handlers require:

- ROPS systems and masted FLT restraint systems.
- An indicator of forward stability with an audible alarm if the load exceeds 95% SWL.

Both rough terrain forklifts and telehandlers require safety devices as follows:

- Outriggers.
- Indicator lamp to show when outriggers are on firm ground.
- Inspection/examination according to **LOLER**.

■ **Dumper Trucks**

Compact dumper trucks require ROPS restraint systems and masted FLT restraint systems.

Safe operation of dumper trucks relies on a safe person strategy and a safe machine strategy.

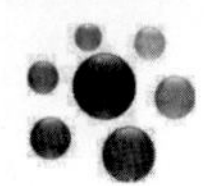

- **Excavators**

  A marked safe working load applies. Stabilisers, where fitted, must have suitable interlocking devices.

  Specific controls exist for:

  - Manually operated load-moving equipment.
  - Lift and hoists.
  - Conveyors.
  - Cranes.

Requirements for Lifting Operations

To meet the requirements of the **Lifting Operations and Lifting Equipment Regulations 1998 (LOLER)**, the operator should ensure that all lifting equipment under their control is:

- Sufficiently **strong, stable** and **suitable** for the proposed use. Similarly, the load and anything attached (e.g. timber pallets and lifting points) must be suitable.
- **Positioned or installed** to prevent the risk of injury, e.g. from the equipment, or the load falling and striking people.
- Visibly **marked** with any appropriate **information** to be taken into account for its safe use, e.g. safe working loads. Accessories, e.g. slings, clamps, etc., should also be marked.

Also, it must be ensured that:

- Lifting operations are **planned, supervised** and **carried out** in a safe manner, by competent people.
- Where equipment is used for **lifting people**, it is marked accordingly. It should also be **safe** for this purpose, i.e. all necessary precautions have been taken to eliminate or reduce any risk.

Examination of Lifting Equipment

LOLER specifies requirements for the testing and inspection of any lifting equipment.

The general requirements are:

- When lifting equipment is used for the first time (or the first time in a new location), it must be thoroughly examined for defects and to ensure correct installation.
- A thorough examination must be conducted:
  - At least every six months, for equipment used for lifting people.
  - At least every twelve months, for all other lifting equipment.
- A competent person must conduct all examinations.
- A report must be provided to the employer, after each inspection.

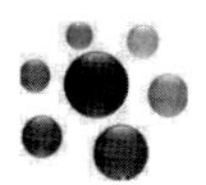

Exam-Style Questions

Short Questions

1. **Outline FOUR** specific types of injury that could foreseeably be caused by the manual handling of loads. (8 marks)

2. **Outline** the **FOUR** main factors to be considered when undertaking a manual handling risk assessment, giving a specific example of each factor. (8 marks)

3. **Outline** the main features of the good lifting technique that should be followed by a worker when lifting a load in order to avoid manual handling injury. (8 marks)

4. When preparing for a lifting operation using a crane, **outline** the main steps to be taken to ensure a safe system of work. (8 marks)

5. (a) **Explain** the meaning of the word 'ergonomics' as used in occupational health and safety practice. (2 marks)
   (b) Poorly designed workstations can cause a range of ill-health effects. **Outline** these ill-health effects. (6 marks)

   (Total: 8 marks)

Long Question

6. (a) **Outline** the **FOUR** main factors to be considered in a manual handling risk assessment. (4 marks)
   (b) **Outline** the steps that should be considered to reduce the risks from manual handling operations and **give** an example in each case. (16 marks)

   (Total: 20 marks)

Model Answers

Short Questions

1. Types of injury associated with manual handling of loads are:
   - Back injuries.
   - Muscle strain and sprain.
   - Hernia.
   - Cuts, abrasions and bruising.
   - Bone injuries.
   - WRULDs.
   - Musculoskeletal disorders.

   (Only four are required.)

2. The four main factors to consider in a manual handling risk assessment are:
   - The load, e.g. is it heavy?
   - The individual, e.g. does the load require unusual strength?
   - The task, e.g. how far is the load to be carried?
   - The environment, e.g. is the floor even?

3. The following are important to ensure good lifting technique:
   - Stop and think.
   - Assess the weight of the load.
   - Bend the knees.
   - Keep the back straight.
   - Establish a good grip.
   - Use of body weight.
   - Keep the load close to the body.
   - Don't twist the body.
   - Position of the feet, shoulders and hips (same direction).

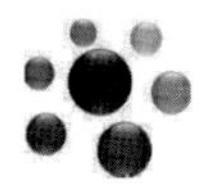

4. The steps to be taken are:
   - Planning the lift.
   - Correct selection of crane.
   - Correct selection of lifting tackle.
   - Ensure the competence of the crane driver and slinger.
   - Ensure there is a valid and current test certificate.

5. (a) Ergonomics means the interface between the person, the equipment and the working environment, and fitting the job to the person.

   (b) Workstations that are poorly designed without considering ergonomics can cause the following ill-health effects:
   - Physical stress due to poor posture.
   - Visual problems due to excessive brightness.
   - Mental stress due to excessive demands.
   - WRULDs - tendonitis, tenosynovitis and carpal tunnel syndrome.

Long Question

6. (a) The four main factors to be considered in a manual handling risk assessment are the:
   - Load.
   - Environment.
   - Task.
   - Individual.

   (b) The steps that should be taken to reduce the risks from manual handling operations are as follows:
   - Eliminate the need to carry out manual handling tasks, e.g. redesign the task to avoid manual handling altogether.
   - If this is not possible, minimise the risk to as low as is reasonably practicable by using mechanical aids, e.g. a trolley to take the weight.
   - Give information, instruction and training to employees, e.g. training in correct lifting technique.
   - Look at environmental conditions, e.g. redesign the workstation to improve access to the load and any equipment used.

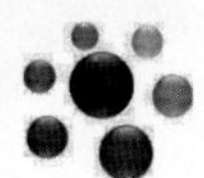

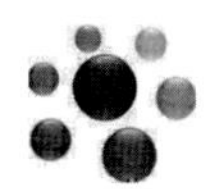

Element 5: Work Equipment Hazards and Risk Control

General Requirements for Work Equipment

The **Provision and Use of Work Equipment Regulations 1998 (PUWER)** set out the general statutory framework to ensure that equipment provided for use at work is safe and is used safely. The **Supply of Machinery (Safety) Regulations 2008** are also relevant.

Work equipment is defined as *"any machinery, appliance, apparatus, tool or installation for use at work (whether exclusively or not)"* and includes:

- Single machines.
- Hand tools.
- Power tools.
- Vehicles.

Suitability of Equipment

The employer must ensure that work equipment:

- Is appropriate for the work to be undertaken.
- Is used in accordance with the manufacturer's specifications and instructions.
- If adapted, is still suitable for its intended purpose.

In addition, the location of equipment must be assessed and it must be designed ergonomically.

Conformity with Relevant Standards and EU Requirements

Under the **Supply of Machinery (Safety) Regulations 2008**, a manufacturer may not supply machinery for use within the EU **unless it is safe** and, in particular:

- It satisfies certain essential health and safety requirements.
- A technical file is compiled.
- Information is provided on its safe operation, e.g. instructions.
- The appropriate conformity assessment procedure has been followed.
- The manufacturer has issued an EC Declaration of Conformity.
- The CE marking has been properly affixed to the machinery.

The act of fixing the CE mark to the product, and signing the Declaration of Conformity, constitutes a declaration by the manufacturer that the product meets the requirements of all the directives which apply to it.

Under **PUWER**, there is also a reciprocal duty on **users** of work equipment to check that it is safe before use.

- **Work equipment presenting specific risks** should only be used by those whose job it is to use it.
- **Information, instruction and training** - all users of work equipment must be informed and trained and young persons should be closely supervised by a competent person.
- **Routine checks and maintenance** must be carried out. Where maintenance involves a specific risk, it must be restricted to trained, designated staff.
- **Examination and inspection** is required:
  - After installation or re-installation.
  - Where deterioration leads to a significant risk.
  - Where exceptional circumstances may jeopardise safety.
  - Records of inspections should be kept.
- **Operation and emergency stop controls**, located at each workstation, are required as specified by **PUWER**. Activating the stop control should override all other controls.
- **Environmental and operating conditions** should ensure that equipment is stable and workstations are well lit, with clear signs warning against risks.
- **Users** of the machines must keep to proper procedures and act in a responsible manner.

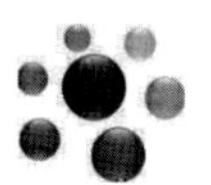

Hand-Held Tools

Hand-held tools cover all types of movable equipment used in the workplace.

Category	Type	Hazards	Injuries	Safe use/control measures
Hand tools	Tools that are entirely powered manually, including axes, wrenches, hammers, chisels, saws, shovels, and picks.	Injuries often due to misuse or operator incompetence.	Mostly contact injuries, where a part of the body strikes, or is hit by, the tool itself.	Appropriate training of operatives and use of PPE. Maintenance and correct storage of tools.
Portable power tools	Hand-held with an external power source (i.e. electricity, compressed air, liquid fuel, hydraulic and power-actuated). Includes electric screwdrivers, pneumatic drills, disc cutters or sanders.	Operator error, misuse and improper maintenance. Risk increased due to presence of power source and speed/force of tool.	Injuries due to puncture wounds, splintering, entanglement in moving machinery and abrasions.	Proper training in the use of tools and use of PPE. Also correct maintenance procedures using serial numbers and logs. Proper storage, particularly for chainsaws and cutting instruments, power leads and hoses.

Procedures for Defective Equipment

Defective or damaged equipment should be taken out of service until repaired. Inspection and any subsequent tests and repairs to damaged or defective equipment should be carried out by a competent person experienced in this type of work. A record of inspection of such equipment should be made and kept for the life of the equipment.

In addition to regular inspections, operators should be instructed never to use damaged or defective equipment. They should visually check equipment before use and withdraw any defective items from service until repaired.

Checks on portable electrical equipment should include:

- Visual inspection of the mains cable for damage.
- Confirm the correct cable for the tool.
- External inspection of the plug.
- Internal inspection of the plug wiring (where appropriate) and fuse - check for the correct rating.

- Cable correctly clamped in the plug and in the tool.
- On/off switch correctly operating and not damaged.
- Outer case undamaged.
- Earth bond test if a metal case.

For **air-fed equipment**, checks should include:

- Air hose connections are properly clamped.
- Hoses are undamaged and do not leak.

Machinery Hazards

Hazards are laid down in **BS EN ISO 12100**.

- **Mechanical hazards** arise from the direct interaction of people with the machines themselves. Hazards are due to the shape, weight, mass and speed of machinery components when in operation. Injuries include:
  - **Crushing** - where the body or part of the body is trapped between two moving parts of a machine or between moving and static objects such that they meet together.
  - **Shearing** - where a part of the body (commonly fingers) is trapped between two parts of a machine, one of which is quickly moving past the other. The effect is like a guillotine, shearing off the trapped body part.
  - **Cutting or severing** - where a sharp-edged part of the machinery comes in contact with the person - for example, the blade of a bandsaw.
  - **Entanglement** - usually an item of clothing gets caught on the rotating part.
  - **Drawing in or trapping** - where a part of the body is caught between two moving parts and drawn into the machine.
  - **Impact** - where a powered part of a machine hits the person.
  - **Stabbing or puncture** - caused by some sharp part of the machine or part of the process (for example, ejected material such as flying swarf or broken tooling) penetrating the person or from cartridge tools, e.g. a nail gun.
  - **Friction or abrasion** - caused by coming into contact with a fast moving surface.
- **Non-mechanical hazards** are the hazards not directly arising from the moving parts of machinery. They arise from or are created by the power sources and the processes for which the machines are used and include:
  - Electricity.
  - Noise.
  - Vibration.
  - Hazardous substances.
  - Ionising radiation.

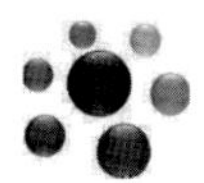

- Non-ionising radiation.
- Extreme temperatures.
- Ergonomics.
- Slips, trips and falls.
- Fire and explosion.

Control Measures for Machinery Hazards

Regulation 11(2) of **PUWER** specifies a hierarchy of protective measures as follows:

- **Fixed guards** - physical barriers preventing access to the hazard. Includes enclosing guards which encase all parts of the hazard and distance guards which reduce access.
- **Interlocking guards** which link the primary guard system to a secondary safety device to complete stoppage or prevent machine operation.
- **Trip devices** which stop or reverse motion when a person enters the hazard area. Trip devices rely on contact being made with a sensor such as a mechanical/ electronic trigger, a photo-electric guard or trip/switch mat.
- **Adjustable guards** need to be manually adjusted to give protection and should only be used if conditions make it impracticable to use another device and where conditions are suitable (i.e. good lighting). They can be easily overridden so operators need to be very careful.
- **Self-adjusting guards** are fixed or movable guards which adjust to the materials being used and are therefore not fully foolproof as blades are temporarily exposed.
- **Two-hand controls** offer a limited means of protecting the hands of an operator where guarding is impracticable.
- **Hold to run controls** have to be held at all times to operate the machine. If the control is released, the equipment will stop. They do not protect any parts while the machine operates and are easily overcome.
- **Emergency stop controls** should bring the machine to a safe stop as quickly as possible and hold in so that the button must be reset before the machine can start again. Release of the stop-button should not restart the machine.
- **Protection appliances**, such as jigs, pushsticks, holders, etc are hand-held tools or hand-controlled fixed devices which allow the operator some control of the work piece but they offer less protection.
- **Personal protective equipment** and clothing will offer immediate and short-term protection but should not be seen as a substitute for guards.
- **Employers** must provide information, instruction, training and supervision.

Strengths, Limitations and Means of Overriding Guard Systems

Type of Guard	Strengths	Weaknesses	Means of Overriding
Fixed	No moving parts. Cannot be interfered with by operator. Virtually maintenance-free.	Machine will still operate with guard removed.	Special tool for removal may be too widely available.
Interlocked	Require some effort to defeat.	Interlock should be designed to fail to safety.	Connectors may be bent out of place. Spare magnets may be used.
Trip devices	Useful when approached by person required as part of job.	Time delay in stopping machine may be too long.	Operators can avoid devices.
Manual adjusting guard	Allows various-sized work pieces to be used.	Relies on people using it properly.	Can be adjusted out of range.
Self-adjusting	Allows various-sized work pieces.	Easily overridden.	Can be adjusted out of range.
Two-handed control	Keeps operator's hands away from moving parts. Rapid manual movement of guard into place.	Protects only operator's hands, not other parts of body or other people.	Two people can override the system by each holding one handle.

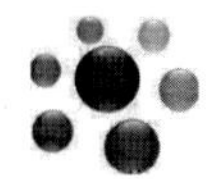

Control Measures for Machinery Hazards

Machinery	Hazards	Control Measures/Protection System
Office Machinery		
Photocopiers	Electricity Dust	Adjustable guard (lid).
Guillotines	Sharp blades	Fixed or adjustable guard depending on the type of work, interlocked guards or trip wires on larger machines.
Document shredders	Entanglement	Interlocked guards and fixed distance guards.
Workshop Machinery		
Abrasive wheels and grinding machines	Bursting discs Contact	Fixed and adjustable guards, PPE (goggles, gloves and ear defenders).
Drills	Entanglement	Trip guards and adjustable guards, PPE (goggles).
Circular saws	Contact with rotating blades Noise Dust	Fixed guards, adjustable guards, LEV, PPE (masks, ear defenders and gloves).
Lathes	Ejection Entanglement	Adjustable guards, PPE (goggles).
Power planer	Contact with rotating blades Noise Dust	Adjustable guards, fixed guards, PPE (masks, ear defenders and gloves).
Spindle moulding machine	Contact with rotating blades Noise	Fixed, interlocked and trip devices.
Robots	Moving parts - unexpected and fast	Fixed perimeter fencing with interlocked access points.
Construction Machinery		
Compressor	Noise Fuel	Fixed guards.
Cement mixer	Fuel/electricity Entanglement	Interlocked and adjustable guards.
Plate compactor	Manual handling Noise Fuel	PPE (gloves, hard hat, ear defenders, safety footwear, high-visibility clothing).
Conveyor systems	Entanglement	Fixed guards, interlocked guards, trip devices.

Ground consolidation equipment	Noise Fuel	PPE (gloves, hard hat, ear defenders, safety footwear, high-visibility clothing).
Circular saw	Moving cutting chain Noise Vibration Fuel	Self-adjusting blade guard, reduced (110v) voltage and safe cable routing, ensure work-piece is securely fixed before sawing, safety goggles, anti-vibration gloves (or time-limitation); dust mask; ear protection, good housekeeping to avoid slips and trips.
Road-marking equipment	Flammable gas cylinders Hot surfaces Fumes	Various - depending on specific equipment.
Electrical generators	Noise Fuel	Various - depending on specific equipment.

Basic Requirements for Guards and Safety Devices

All guarding systems should:

- Be compatible with process.
- Be of adequate strength.
- Be maintained.
- Allow maintenance without removal.
- Not increase risk or restrict view.
- Not be easily bypassed.

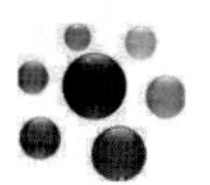

Exam-Style Questions

Short Questions

1. With reference to the **Provision and Use of Work Equipment Regulations 1998**, **outline** the factors that would ensure a piece of work equipment is suitable for use. (8 marks)

2. **Outline** control strategy for the safe use of hand-held tools. (8 marks)

3. **Identify FOUR** mechanical hazards associated with machinery, giving an example in each case. (8 marks)

4. **Outline FOUR** non-mechanical hazards associated with machinery, giving an example in each case. (8 marks)

5. **Outline FOUR** guarding methods for machinery, giving an example in each case. (8 marks)

Long Question

6. **Describe FIVE** non-mechanical hazards associated with machinery and how to minimise the risks associated with **EACH** of these hazards. (20 marks)

Model Answers

Short Questions

1. To ensure that a piece of work equipment is suitable for use, it must:

    - Be capable of being maintained.
    - Be provided with information and instructions for use.
    - Have an appropriate control system with start, stop and emergency controls.
    - Meet the requirements of EU standards and be CE marked.
    - Have appropriate lighting.
    - Have appropriate warning signs.
    - Be stable.

2. A control strategy for the safe use of hand-held tools consists of:

    - Appropriate training.
    - Correct maintenance.
    - Visual checks.
    - Appropriate PPE.

3. Mechanical hazards associated with machinery are:

    - Crushing, e.g. trapping a finger between moving parts when opening a photocopier.
    - Shearing, e.g. trapping a finger while using an office guillotine.
    - Cutting or severing, e.g. coming into contact with the blade of a bandsaw.
    - Entanglement, e.g. a loose cuff getting caught in an abrasive wheel.
    - Drawing in, e.g. a finger being drawn in while using a document shredder.
    - Impact, e.g. with a robot making unanticipated movements.
    - Stabbing or puncture, e.g. by a sewing machine needle.
    - Friction or abrasion, e.g. coming into contact with a sander.

    (Only four are required.)

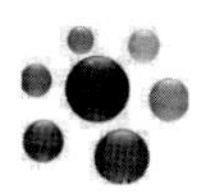

4. Non-mechanical hazards associated with machinery are:
    - Noise, e.g. from a cylinder mower, leading to temporary hearing loss.
    - Vibration, e.g. from a chainsaw, leading to vascular disorders.
    - Electricity, e.g. a faulty drill, causing electric shock or burns.
    - Temperature, e.g. burns from a cutting torch.
    - Radiation, e.g. from an X-ray machine, leading to the development of cancer.
    - Substances, e.g. inhaling sawdust from the working process.
    - Ergonomics, e.g. stress from the need to keep pace with a conveyor system.

    (Only four are required.)

5. The following are guarding methods for machinery:
    - Fixed guard, e.g. to enclose a belt-drive mechanism.
    - Distance guard, e.g. a fixed perimeter fence round a machine.
    - Interlocking guard, e.g. to protect from the cutting operation of a lathe.
    - Trip device, e.g. a trip bar guard fitted to a pillar drill.
    - Adjustable guard, e.g. for the cutter on a milling machine.
    - Self-adjusting guard, e.g. on a metal-cutting saw.
    - Two-handed control, e.g. on a power press.

    (Only four are required.)

Long Question

6.

Non-Mechanical Hazard	Minimising the Risks
Noise	Engineering controls
Vibration	Maintenance - padded mounts
Substances	Enclosure
Electricity	Double insulation, earthing, fuses, etc.
Temperature	Use of PPE
Ergonomics	Use of anthropometrics
Radiation	Signage, use of PPE, and training

(Only five hazards and corresponding risk minimisation measures were required.)

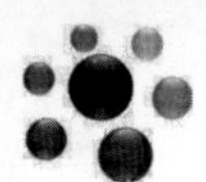

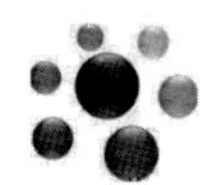

Element 6: Electrical Safety

Hazards and Risks Associated with Electricity at Work

Principles of Electricity

Electricity is a form of energy associated with the flow of charged particles from one point to another through a conductor. There must be an unbroken path between the two points through which the particles can travel - the complete path being known as the **circuit**. A switch can be used to complete or break the circuit.

- **Voltage** measures the flow of electricity between two terminals.
- **Current** is the flow or speed at which power travels along a conductor and it is measured in amperes.
- **Resistance** is a measure of how much a circuit or components in a circuit restricts the flow of electrical current. Resistors are components designed to reduce the amount of current that travels through a particular part of a circuit.

Basic Circuitry

Electrical circuits are a collection of components such as resistors and diodes that are linked by conducting wires and cables. Current flows through conducting wires between components and each component affects the movement of the current. Insulating materials (i.e. rubber, plastic) enclose the wires to prevent current leaking out and conductors touching and causing a **short circuit**.

- **Earthed conductors** provide a safe path for any current to dissipate to earth in a fault situation.
- **Direct Current (DC)** is current flowing in one direction, e.g. a battery.
- **Alternating Current (AC)** flow alters at regular intervals.

Risks of Electricity

Electric Shock

An electric shock is received when a person makes contact with a live conductor and the current passes through his/her body. The body acts as the conductor for the current, interrupting the circuit and providing an alternative path for it to flow. Shock injury from DC is generally less severe than that from AC.

- **Effects on the Body**

  An electric shock results in a convulsive response by the nervous system to the passage of electricity through that part of the body. This causes the muscles to contract, often violently. At its most serious, current passing through the heart may interfere with the heart rate and cause fibrillation and/or cardiac arrest. Current may also interfere with the muscles controlling breathing and cause respiratory failure. Both of these cases may be fatal.

- **Factors Affecting Severity**

  The severity of the shock and type of injury caused will depend on:

  - Voltage of current.
  - Frequency of current.
  - Duration of contact with conductor.
  - Current path through body.
  - Resistance.
  - Contact surface area.
  - Environment.

- **Electrical Burns**

  The heat given off by the current will cause **direct burns** at the point of contact, point of exit from the body and possibly on internal organs. **Indirect burns** or arcing will occur where an uninsulated live conductor comes into contact with another earthed conductor. **Arcing** generates ultraviolet radiation which can burn the skin and retina of the eye (causing **arc eye** or eye flash).

- **Common Causes of Electrical Fires**

  In order for a fire to start, a source of heat is needed and electricity can do this in three ways:

  - **Arcing** - the generation of electrical sparks or arcs between an uninsulated or poorly insulated conductor and another, earthed conductor.
  - **Overheating of conductors** - due to poor or inadequate insulation allowing the natural heat created by the flow of electricity to escape.
  - **Static electrical discharge** - sparks generated by static build up especially dangerous where flammable dusts or vapours are present.

  Electrical fires can be very dangerous because it is not possible to use water to extinguish them. Water is a good conductor of electricity and its use would create a live electrical hazard.

Workplace Electrical Equipment

Nearly a quarter of all reportable electrical accidents involve portable equipment and most of these accidents result in electric shock.

Causes of **workplace electrical equipment accidents** include:

- Using unsuitable equipment.
- Using equipment in wet, damp or humid conditions.
- Misuse.

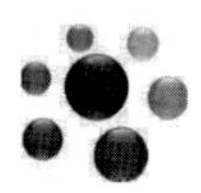

- Physical abuse.
- Carrying out unauthorised repairs.
- Continuing to use the equipment knowing it is faulty or defective.
- Chemical damage to the flex or tool from harsh chemicals.
- Lack of routine inspection, maintenance or testing.

Secondary Hazards

As well as any injuries caused directly by an electric shock, secondary hazards can arise, based on what the person was doing when they received the shock, or when a short circuit occurred, e.g. a person working on a ladder receives a shock and the shock throws them from the ladder to the ground, or into the path of a moving vehicle.

High Risks Associated with Electricity

Certain occasions and types of work activity greatly increase the risks associated with electricity, such as:

- Poorly maintained electrical equipment.
- Contact with underground cables.
- Work on mains electricity supplies (230v).
- Work on live or dead electrical supplies.
- Use of electrical equipment in wet or flammable atmospheres.

Control Measures

Selection and Suitability of Equipment for Use in Construction Activities

Safe handling of electrical equipment in normal conditions depends on:

- Selecting equipment designed for the purpose and place it is to be used in. This will include considering the hazardous environments (i.e. extreme weather and temperature; natural hazards; contact with corrosive or flammable substances) equipment might be used in.
- Using the equipment according to manufacturers' recommendations and not exceeding the electrical strength and capability of the equipment.
- Protection of conductors and using suitable protective devices, fuses, earthing, etc.
- Assessing any likely mechanical damage and carrying out effective inspection and maintenance routines.
- Use of competent persons.
- Use of safe systems of work, e.g. for buried services.

Planning and Installation

Plans for the distribution of electricity supplies on site should be drawn up and work carried out by competent persons. All wiring and installations, whether permanent or temporary (e.g. site offices, accommodation), should conform with the latest **IEE (Institution of Electrical Engineers) Regulations** and relevant standards, e.g. **BS 7575**, **4343**, **4363**, **5378**.

Permit-to-Work Procedures and Requirements

An electrical permit-to-work is a statement that a circuit or item of equipment/plant is safe to work on. Separate permits are required for different tasks, e.g. hot work, low or high-voltage work. Permits should include details of:

- Equipment and plant that is to be used, isolated and/or worked on.
- The work to be carried out, e.g. maintenance, inspection.
- Likely hazards and necessary precautions, including the competent person/persons who will carry out the work.

A typical electrical permit-to-work has a number of elements, for example:

- Title and permit number.
- Reference to other permits/isolation certificates in place.
- Equipment, distribution board, circuit or job location, and plant identification.
- Description and nature of the electrical work to be carried out.
- Hazards identified and precautions necessary.
- Protective equipment and PPE required.
- Authorisation that it's safe to work.
- Date, time and duration of the permit.
- Identification of employees in control of the work.
- Permit acceptance - by those doing the work.
- Considerations for extending the terms of the permit.
- Returning to service on completion of work.
- Cancellation certifying that testing has been carried out and the plant satisfactorily re-commissioned.

Permits-to-work must be audited and inspected at regular intervals to ensure the validity of the procedures in place and that the documents and records kept are completed accurately.

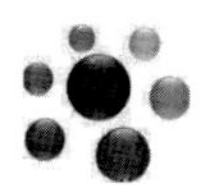

Requirements of Temporary Electrical Supplies

Electrical systems and equipment for use on construction sites should withstand the conditions of the site; be designed and manufactured to suitable standards; have suitable for repeated use on various contracts; be easy to transport and store; be robust and resist damage; and have lockable switches and means of safe isolation.

Electrical sockets used on construction sites must be specified - those for domestic use are not adequate. Temporary supply equipment should undergo regular visual examination and test by a competent person.

Protective Systems - Advantages and Limitations

Protective devices incorporated into electrical circuits or the equipment itself serve to cut off the electricity supply in the event of a fault and/or to reduce the strength of an electric shock should someone come into contact with the power supply.

- **Fuse** - a weak link in the circuit.
- **Circuit breaker** - a mechanical switch which automatically opens when the circuit is overloaded.
- **Earthing** - a low resistance path to earth for fault current.
- **Isolation** - cutting the power.
- **Reduced low voltage** - so that less current flows during an electric shock accident.
- **Residual Current Devices** (RCDs) - sensitive and fast acting trips.
- **Double insulation** - separating people from the conductors using two layers of insulation.

These protective systems have advantages and disadvantages. Portable electrical appliances should undergo user checks, formal visual inspections and combined inspection and testing to ensure electrical safety.

Use of Competent Persons

"A person is accepted as competent where he has sufficient training and experience or knowledge and other qualities to enable him to properly do the task in question."
(MHSWR 1999).

Health and safety legislation requires that work on electrical systems and equipment, such as inspection and testing, is carried out by competent persons.

Where employees are not instructed on and trained in the safe implementation of safe systems of work for electrical systems and circuits they should only work under the supervision of a competent person.

Use of Safe Systems of Work

Live Working

Work on or near to an electrical system *"shall be carried out in such a manner as not to give rise, so far as is reasonably practicable, to danger".* Such work includes examination and testing. (**Electricity at Work Regulations 1989** (Regulation 4)).

No live work should be carried out unless:

- it is unreasonable for the equipment to be dead; **and**
- it is reasonable for the work to take place on or near the live conductors; **and**
- suitable precautions have been taken to prevent injury.

These conditions must all be met for work on or near live conductors to be carried out. Dead working should be the normal method used.

Safe Isolation

Adequate precautions must be taken to ensure that electrical equipment made dead cannot be switched on again during work. This is known as "isolation".

Isolation is *"...the disconnection and separation of the electrical equipment from every source of electrical energy in such a way that this disconnection and separation is secure"* (**Electricity at Work Regulations 1989**).

Isolation should be carried out by a competent person.

On a construction site it is essential to isolate and prove dead any secondary source, e.g. generators.

Locating Buried Services

Before digging or excavating, site plans should be checked or electronic locator devices used to see if any buried services are in close proximity. When working close to a known buried cable, mechanical diggers should stop and hand-digging begin, proceeding with care until the cable is discovered. All cables, when revealed, should be marked.

Overhead Cables

Overhead cables should be measured and goalposts or flag-banners used to identify the cables. Where possible, overhead supplies should be taken down, re-routed or turned off.

All points that pass beneath cables should be signed and lit if work carried on at night.

When fitting overhead cables they should be supported with steel-wire and securely anchored at each end.

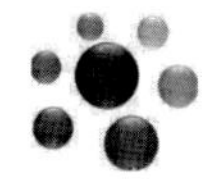

Inspection and Maintenance Strategies

To ensure safety when any electrical equipment is used, it is important that it is regularly inspected and maintained. This involves:

- Identifying which equipment has to be maintained and where/how it is to be used.
- Discouraging 'unauthorised' equipment in the workplace.
- Carrying out simple **user checks** for signs of damage - e.g. casing, plug pins and cable sheath.
- A competent person carrying out **formal visual inspections** routinely and **periodic testing** of the equipment.
- Following systems for the reporting and replacement of defective equipment.
- Recording all maintenance and test results along with the inventory of equipment in use.

Deciding on the **frequency of maintenance** should be based on an assessment of risk to be undertaken as part of the assessment of risks under the **Management of Health and Safety at Work Regulations 1999**. Factors to consider when making the assessment include:

- Legal standards and codes of practice.
- Type of equipment and whether or not it is hand-held.

- Manufacturer's recommendations.
- Initial integrity, soundness and age of the equipment.
- Working environment in which the equipment is used (such as whether it is wet or dusty) or the likelihood of mechanical damage.
- Frequency of use and the duty cycle of the equipment.
- Foreseeable abuse.
- Effects of any modifications or repairs to the equipment.
- Analysis of previous records of maintenance, including both formal inspection and combined inspection and testing.

Advantages and Limitations of Portable Appliance Testing

A Portable Appliance Testing (PAT) device carries out (and, in some cases, records) detailed tests automatically. It is generally used in combination with visual inspection.

- Advantages:
  - Will detect unseen problems, e.g. deterioration of insulation and earth faults.
  - Allow early removal of faulty items.
  - Demonstrate legal compliance.
  - Trends or patterns in faults may be spotted.
- Limitations:
  - Requires knowledge of equipment and testing equipment.
  - Proves safety only at the time of testing.
  - Does not ensure safe use or prevent misuse.
  - Items may be missed and remain unsafe.
  - May not be suitable for all equipment.

Emergency Procedures

First-Aid Treatment for Electric Shock

- Break the current between the victim and the electricity source; isolate or separate the victim from the current with a non-conductive material.
- Artificial respiration should commence as soon as the current has been isolated and continue until the victim recovers or qualified medical personnel intervene.
- If there is a risk of electric shock in your workplace, first aiders should be trained in resuscitation methods.
- Emergency services should always be called, as there is a risk of internal injuries that are not visible.
- First-aid treatment may be required for electrical burns sustained.

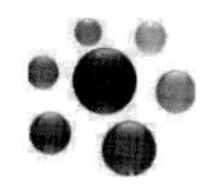

Control Measures for Working Near Overhead Power Lines

Be sure you can reproduce this or a similar diagram in response to an examination question.

Work under or near overhead power lines should be avoided. Where the work cannot be avoided, the **consultation with the supply authority** is necessary.

Three situations generally arise in construction at overhead power lines:

1. No scheduled work or passage of plant will take place under the lines.
2. Plant and equipment will pass under the lines.
3. Work will be carried out beneath the lines.

- **No Scheduled Work or Passage of Plant Under the Lines:**
  - Ground level barriers.
  - Conspicuous marking, flags/bunting.
  - Consider possible jib length.
  - Barriers either side, no storage
- **Plant/Equipment Passing Under the Lines:**
  - Minimum number of passageways.
  - Goal posts used with warning notices.
  - Illuminated signs after dark.
- **Work Carried Out Beneath the Lines:**
  - Additional precautions to stop upward movement of jibs, poles, etc.
  - Possibly exclude mobile equipment, etc.
  - Use limiters on height adjustments of equipment.
  - Use roof over area to restrict.

Specific requirements for work near overhead electric lines are contained in the **Electricity at Work Regulations 1989**.

Exam-Style Questions

Short Questions

1. **Outline** the first-aid treatment that might be appropriate to give a worker who has received a significant electric shock at work. (8 marks)

2. **Identify FOUR** protective systems that can be incorporated into an electrical circuit and describe how each protective system enhances safety. (8 marks)

3. **Outline** the things that a user should check when carrying out the visual inspection of a portable electrical appliance. (8 marks)

4. **Outline FOUR** general management principles relating to the safety of electrical appliances. (8 marks)

Long Question

5. In relation to the use of mains voltage (230V), hand-held electrical tools:
   (a) **Outline** the possible hazards associated with the use of such tools. (8 marks)
   (b) **Describe** suitable preventive and protective measures which should be taken to control the risks associated with the use of such tools. (12 marks)

   (Total: 20 marks)

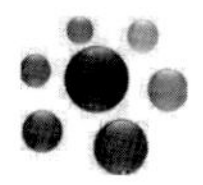

Model Answers

Short Questions

1. Following an electric shock:

   - Break any contact using non-conductive material or isolate the supply.
   - Artificial respiration should commence immediately and continue until either the victim recovers or medical staff intervene.
   - Emergency medical attention should always be sought, as there is a risk of internal injury.

2. The following protective systems can be incorporated within an electrical circuit:

   - Fuse - acts as a weak link.
   - Circuit breaker - acts as a weak link.
   - Earthing - prevents current from being carried.
   - Isolation - physically separates the electricity from the power source.
   - Switching off - deprives the equipment of power whilst remaining connected to the supply.
   - Low voltage using a transformer - reduces the effect of any shock.
   - Residual current device.
   - Double insulation - encloses the item from danger.

   (Only four are required.)

3. The following user checks should be applied to a portable electrical appliance:

   - Check the cable for damage.
   - Check for damage to the plug or cable, e.g. cracks, taped repairs.
   - Check the cable into the plug.
   - Check the condition of the casing.
   - Check that the on/off controls work.
   - Visually check the fuse rating.
   - Check the test label date.

4. General management principles relating to the safety of electrical appliances are:
   - Proper selection of suitable equipment.
   - The use of protective devices.
   - Effective inspection and maintenance by competent persons.
   - Visual user checks.

Long Question

5. (a) Possible hazards when using 230V, hand-held electrical tools are:
   - Electric shock.
   - Burns.
   - Arcing.
   - Explosion.
   - Secondary effects, such as falls.

   (b) The following preventive and protective measures should be taken to control such hazards:
   - Reduced voltage.
   - Fuses.
   - Residual current devices.
   - Earthing.
   - Double insulation.
   - Testing.
   - Visual inspection.
   - Favourable environmental conditions.

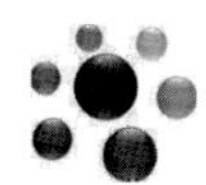

Element 7: Fire Safety

Principles of Fire Initiation, Classification and Spread and Fire Risks Caused by Construction Activities

Basic Principles of Fire

Before a fire can start, the following three components must be present in sufficient quantity:

- **Heat** is the source of ignition - whether a flame or spark or the heat resulting from these processes.
- **Fuel** includes any combustible material (i.e. paper, wood, dusts, gases, etc.).
- **Oxygen** in minimum quantities must be present to support a fire.

Extinguishing a fire is based on removing one or more sides of the fire triangle.

- Removing the fuel - **starvation**.
- Removing the oxygen - **smothering**.
- Removing the heat - **cooling**.

Classification of Fire

Fires are usually classified by fuel types:

- **Class A** - solid, combustible material such as paper or wood.
- **Class B** - flammable liquids like petrol, oil, grease, fats and paint.
- **Class C** - gases (i.e. methane, propane and natural gas).
- **Class D** - metals (i.e. aluminium, sodium, potassium, magnesium).
- **Class F** - cooking fats such as chip pan fires.

Basic Principles of Heat Transmission and Fire Spread

Fire can be spread by:

- **Convection** where hot air rises then cools and falls, causing an air flow that spreads a fire rapidly.
- **Conduction** where heat is transferred through solid materials (conductors).
- **Radiation** where heat travels through the air from a source and may ignite any fabric or material.
- **Direct burning** where contact is direct from one source to another.

Additionally, burning embers can also be carried by the wind, allowing fire to spread from one location to another.

Construction sites contain many ignition sources including hot work, electricity, smoking, cooking appliances, unsafe storage of flammable materials, mechanical heat (friction) and arson (deliberate ignition).

In the uncompleted phases of a structure the normal structural fire precautions are not present, e.g. fire doors. Also, security is lower and risk of arson higher.

Fire Risk Assessment

The Regulatory Reform (Fire Safety) Order 2005 (RRFSO)

The **RRFSO** came into effect in England and Wales on 1 October 2006 and introduced two new terms:

- **Responsible Person:**
  - The employer, for some, or all parts of the premises.
  - The owner or agent, for shared parts of the premises or for shared fire safety systems.
  - The occupier, if they have control over the premises.
  - The self-employed, if they have control over the premises.
  - **Anyone** who has a level of control over all, or part of the premises.

  Where there is more than one responsible person (e.g. a shared premises), each must co-operate with the others, as far as is necessary, to comply with the requirements of the **RRFSO**.

- **Relevant Person:**

  This means anyone who by law may be on the premises or nearby, and may be at risk in the event of fire.

There are basic requirements that **must** be addressed by all 'responsible persons':

- Conduct a fire risk assessment for the premises over which you have control.
- Identify the fire hazards and risks associated with the premises, materials/ substances, activities, etc.
- Identify the people (or groups of people) at risk, and anyone who may be especially at risk.
- Remove or reduce the risks, as far as reasonably practicable.
- Put in place general fire precautions to deal with any remaining risks.
- Implement additional preventive and protective measures, if flammable or explosive substances are used or stored on the premises.
- Develop and implement appropriate emergency procedures.

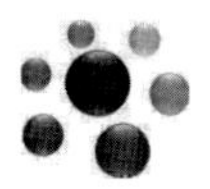

- Record the significant findings of the risk assessment and actions you have taken to remove/reduce risk.
- Review the risk assessment periodically, or after significant changes in the workplace, or when there is reason to believe it may no longer be valid.

Enforcement of the requirements of RRFSO is principally the responsibility of:

- The Fire and Rescue Authority:
  - For the majority of workplaces.
- The Health and Safety Executive:
  - Construction sites.
  - Nuclear installations.
  - Ships (under construction/repair).
- Local Authorities:
  - Sports grounds.

The most common means of enforcement is the issue of Notices by Inspectors.

Conducting a Fire Risk Assessment

- **Step 1: Identify the fire hazards**.
- **Step 2: Identify the people at risk**.
- **Step 3: Evaluate the fire risks, remove or reduce the risks and protect people from any remaining risk**.
  - Consider the likelihood of fire breaking out and the consequences (severity) of any harm likely to be caused.
- **Step 4: Record the significant findings and actions taken to remove and/or reduce risk**.
  - Develop and implement an appropriate **Emergency Plan**.
  - **Inform and instruct** relevant persons on the actions to be taken in the event of a fire.
  - **Train** employees, particularly those with specific duties, e.g. fire marshals.
- **Step 5: Review**.

  The fire risk assessment must be reviewed:

  - **Whenever** there is reason to suspect that it may no longer be valid, e.g. after a significant incident or 'near-miss'.
  - If there has been a significant change in circumstances in the workplace, e.g. changes to plant, equipment, processes, substances used, personnel, etc.
  - Periodically - the frequency should depend on the nature of the business and the fire risks.

The fire risk assessment should include a **site specific emergency plan**, locating all main fire hazards and protective measures on site. It should be kept in the Construction Phase Plan. The precautions identified will become part of the site induction training and evacuation procedure for all parties.

Fire Prevention and Prevention of Fire Spread

Control Measures to Minimise the Risk of Fire in a Construction Workplace

- **Use and Storage of Flammable and Combustible Materials**

  Flammable and other substances that pose a risk of fire or explosion must be stored, transported and used appropriately. Where possible, use of flammable and combustible materials should be eliminated or reduced using the hierarchy of controls.

  Storage of flammable substances should be:

  - Securely fenced, ventilated buildings or open-air compounds; separate from other parts of site and away from emergency exits.
  - Accessible to fire-fighters.
  - Properly marked/signed.
  - Provided with two escape routes.
  - Large enough to allow clear spaces to be maintained around stacks of materials, taking care that the stacked materials themselves do not cause a hazard.

- **Control of Ignition Sources**

  Construction work can in some cases alter the flammability of substances used and appropriate precautions need to be taken. The implementation of safe working systems and practices (i.e. 'no smoking' policies or designated smoking areas; good housekeeping; no bonfires on site or on windy days) can help prevent fires due to accidental ignition.

- **Control of Hot Work**

  Welding, flame cutting, use of blow lamps or portable grinding equipment can pose a serious fire hazard and need to be strictly controlled when carried out in areas near flammable materials. This can be done by having a written permit-to-work system for all workers involved, i.e. employees and contractors.

- **Safe Systems of Work**

  Most workplaces use processes and equipment which produce sufficient heat to act as a source of ignition given the right circumstances. Inadequate safeguarding of electrical equipment and systems, and electrical faults following inefficient maintenance can also give rise to fires. Good working practices can minimise the risk of fire.

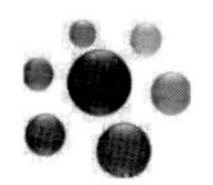

- **Permit-to-Work Procedures**

  On-site construction activities, e.g. welding, flame cutting, use of blow lamps or bitumen boilers, soldering equipment and portable grinding equipment can pose serious fire hazards which can be strictly controlled by using a written permit-to-work system.

  A hot work permit should include information on:

  - Atmosphere testing requirements.
  - Fire-fighting equipment to be available in the work area.
  - The permitted time span of the activity and the level of supervision required.
  - Actions to be taken when work stops or is finished (i.e. all hot work equipment to be removed from a confined space).
  - Flammable gases and oxygen cylinders not to be taken into confined spaces to avoid fires or explosions due to leaks.

- **Safe Storage, Transport and Use of Cylinder Gases**

  The **Dangerous Substances and Explosive Atmospheres Regulations (DSEAR) 2002** require an employer to carry out a suitable and sufficient assessment of the risks to employees where dangerous substances are or may be present in the workplace. LPG contained in cylinders should be stored upright (unless designed otherwise), with the valves uppermost and kept in open air positions protected from sunlight or from falling materials.

  Storage areas should be safe and well ventilated, constructed of non-combustible material, and well signed/marked with warning signs. LPG should not be stored beneath overhead power cables and cylinders should be clearly marked 'Highly Flammable LPG', with the design pressure and temperature. The design and construction of such cylinders is detailed in the **Pressure Systems Safety Regulations 2000**.

  Cylinders on site should be transported using suitable trolleys to avoid manual handling problems, and by cranes using a special carrier. Transportation by vehicle should only be undertaken if it is suitable and fit for the purpose, e.g. not in an enclosed van but secured from undue movement in an upright position. The use of any LPG plant equipment should take into account any possible overheating of adjacent/local areas and the nearby use of any equipment such as hand-held tools and tar boilers which could cause ignition.

- **Good Housekeeping**

  High standards of housekeeping will ensure that combustible materials and waste do not present a fire risk. Workstations and storage areas should be kept tidy to ensure combustible materials do not come into contact with ignition and heat sources.

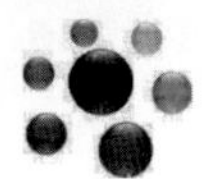

Storage of Small Quantities of Flammable Liquids

Correct storage and use of highly flammable liquids will prevent accidental ignition or explosion. Non-flammable substances should be used in preference wherever possible but where flammable liquids are used, these must be correctly labelled and used in a well ventilated area and in small quantities to reduce the risk of spillages. Small quantities of up to 50 litres of flammable materials, e.g. paints, solvents, adhesives can be stored in lockable steel chests.

Structural Measures to Prevent the Spread of Fire and Smoke

Building design can significantly reduce the risk of fire starting or spreading. Buildings can consist of:

- Compartments or cells to contain fire (keep it in).
- Compartments or cells to keep fire out.

Common Building Materials

- **Steel**-framed buildings are very strong although steel will quickly lose its structural strength during a fire due to it being a good conductor. Enclosing structural steel in concrete will minimise this risk.
- **Timber** is highly combustible but can be protected by plasterboard to minimise this risk. Fire resistance of timber relies on the '4 Ts': thickness, tightness, type and treatment.
- **Bricks** are normally made in a furnace so they are able to withstand high temperatures.
- **Building blocks** and **boards** have a high fire resistance although some older boards may contain asbestos.
- **Glass** and **double glazing** can shatter during a fire although fire-resistant glazing has been developed.
- Most **paints** contain flammable elements that can spread fire and smoke.
- **Plastics** may not fully combust but they give off smoke that may be toxic.
- Most modern **insulating materials** are non-combustible but in many older buildings combustible materials (such as sawdust) have been used and can help fire spread considerably.

Protection of Openings and Voids

Ceiling and floor voids, as well as openings around pipe-work and ventilation ducts can allow air to feed and spread fire. Debris should not be allowed to accumulate in voids and openings should be bonded or fire-stopped with non-combustible material.

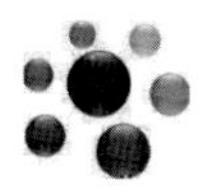

Fire doors and protected corridors must give a minimum of 60 minutes protection from fire and smoke. They must be maintained to ensure a fire seal is securely in place when the door is closed.

Use of Suitable Electrical Equipment in Flammable Atmospheres

Work in flammable atmospheres must be carefully controlled to avoid fire or explosion. Hazardous atmospheres are allocated a zone; these zones determine the types of work equipment which can be used:

Hazardous Atmosphere Zone	Category of Equipment
Zone 0 - explosive gas atmosphere present continuously or for long periods	**Cat 1 Electrical equipment:** - "ia" intrinsically safe - EN 50020 2002 - Ex s - special protection if specifically certified for Zone 0
Zone 1 - explosive gas atmosphere likely to occur in normal operation	**Cat 2 Electrical equipment:** - "d" flameproof enclosure - EN 50018 2000
Zone 2 - explosive gas atmosphere not likely to occur in normal operation; if it does it is only for short time	**Cat 3 Electrical equipment:** - Electrical type n - EN 50021 1999

Fire Detection, Fire Alarm and Fire-Fighting Equipment

Fire Detection

In the simplest of workplaces, fire detection can rely on nothing more than a person seeing or smelling the fire. Where early detection is critical, detection systems should be used:

- **Smoke/Fume - Detectors**

  Very common. Will detect small particles in smoke, are very sensitive and give early warning. They have ionising or optical sensors, but can give false alarms in humid, dusty or smoky atmospheres.

- **Heat Detectors**

  More suitable for some situations. Detect heat from a fire, but are less sensitive and give later warnings. They can detect heat by fixed temperature or the rate of rise in temperature (fusion or expansion heat detectors). They may not detect a slow, smouldering fire giving off smoke but little heat.

- **Flame Detectors**

  These are optical sensors and will detect flames by ultraviolet and infrared systems.

Fire Alarms

All workplaces must have a means of sounding an alarm in a fire situation. Systems can be manual or automatic.

- **Manual systems** - suitable for small workplaces of low risk; can only raise the alarm over a limited area/time; should be made general, e.g. using a phone or public address system, or a manual/electric system.
- **Interlinked smoke alarms** - used in remote locations; detect the smoke (or flames) and sound an alarm; not just stand-alone, but often in a linked circuit.
- **Manual/electric systems** - initiated from an alarm call point; when pressed, alarm sounded throughout premises; may also relay an alert to the fire service.
- **Automatic fire alarms** - not normally present on small construction sites; made up of automatic detectors and manual call points linked through a central control box to alarms. A person can activate them on seeing a fire, or they will initiate automatically if no-one is around.

Portable Fire-Fighting Equipment

Extinguishing Media

- **Fire blankets** - designed to smother a variety of different small fires. Usually come in a red box or wrapping.
- **Hose reels** - sited in fixed locations in buildings to fight larger fires.
- **Sprinklers** - usually activated automatically by thermal detectors. Can help control fire in a contained area.
- **Fire extinguishers** are coloured red, with an identifying colour code to denote the extinguishing agent contained:

Type	Use	Markings
Water	Class A combustible fires	Red
Foam	Class A and B fires	Cream
Dry powder	Class B and C fires	Blue
Carbon dioxide	Class B and electrical fires	Black

Regular **inspections and examinations** must be carried out by a suitably qualified technician.

Personnel should be familiar with the available fire-fighting equipment and **trained** to use it correctly.

Portable fire-fighting equipment should be readily **visible and properly mounted** along escape routes, at an appropriate distance from any potential fire risk. There would normally be a minimum of two locations on any floor.

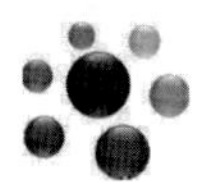

Advantages and Limitations of Extinguishing Media

All extinguishers have short duration and relatively small amount of extinguishing agent - so are only suitable for small fires.

Other advantages and limitations include:

Extinguishing Agent	Advantages	Limitations
Water	Good cooling medium for Class A fires No chemicals involved Inexpensive material	Not suitable on Class B, D or F fires or on live electrical equipment
Carbon dioxide	Smothers quickly Non-toxic Suitable for Class A and B fires and live electrical equipment	A gas cylinder under pressure Not suitable on Class D fires Use with care - rapidly exhausting gas can cause freeze-injury if touched Noisy and can startle a user
Foam	Suitable for Class A and B fires Smothers a fire Valuable where burning liquids are 'running' (moving along the ground, as in a spillage)	Not suitable for Class C, D or F fires Messy Not easy to correctly use unless trained
Dry powder	Suitable for all classes of fires and on live electrical equipment Smothers a fire	Can be messy Some noise when exhausting the powder
Vaporising liquid	Suitable for Class A and B fires, especially live electrical equipment Smothers a fire and interferes chemically with the combustion process	Expensive medium Uses gas cylinder under pressure Noisy when released Some can be harmful if inhaled

Means of Escape

Generally, most workplaces should provide **alternative means of escape** so that people do not have to pass through hazardous areas to reach safety. An escape route provides the means by which occupants of a specified area can reach a place of safety - a protected area where there is no fire risk, or the risk is considerably reduced. This **place of safety** will be an assembly area under the evacuation procedure.

- **Stairs** and **passageways** should be kept clear, well lit and appropriately marked.
- **Doors** on an escape route should open in the direction of travel and they should be maintained to ensure an effective smoke seal. There should be toughened glass vision panels in the doors.
- **Emergency lighting**, if provided, should be regularly tested and maintained and should be backed up by an emergency power supply.
- **Exit** and **directional signs** should comply with **Health and Safety (Safety Signs and Signals) Regulations 1996**.
- **Assembly points** are safe refuge areas in a building or in the open air. They should be clearly marked and kept clear.

Evacuation of a Construction Workplace

Emergency Evacuation Procedures

These should be written into the company health and safety policy and fire evacuation notices should be displayed at each exit point. The evacuation plan should make provision for staff with hearing or other physical disabilities, children and the elderly.

Fire marshals or designated persons should be appointed to take responsibility in a fire situation. Their duties would include:

- Checking that all areas in the premises have been evacuated.
- Shutting windows and ventilation systems (i.e. air conditioning).
- Switching off electrical appliances.
- Passing the emergency plan to the fire services.
- Conducting a **roll call** at the assembly point and giving emergency services details of any missing persons.

Fire drills are practice evacuations that should take place at least once a year and preferably more frequently in areas of high risk. All staff must be aware of, and be **trained** in using, the correct procedure to follow in the event of fire.

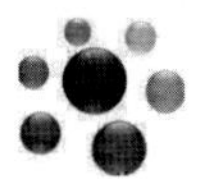

Exam-Style Questions

Short Questions

1. **Describe** the three components of the fire triangle. (8 marks)

2. **Describe FOUR** classes of fire and explain what they involve. (8 marks)

3. (a) **Describe** the class of fire a water extinguisher would be suitable for. (2 marks)
   (b) **Describe** the class of fire a foam extinguisher would be suitable for. (2 marks)
   (c) **Describe** the class of fire a CO_2 extinguisher would be suitable for. (2 marks)
   (d) **Outline** the type of extinguisher that would be appropriate for use on flammable metals. (2 marks)
   (Total: 8 marks)

4. **Outline** the four main methods of heat transfer that may be involved in the spread of fire within a building. (8 marks)

5. **Outline** the safe storage requirements for flammable and highly flammable liquids to be stored both inside and outside of buildings. (8 marks)

Long Question

6. (a) **Describe** the **FOUR** methods of heat transfer by which fire can spread in the workplace. (8 marks)
   (b) **Outline** the principal characteristics of a safe means of escape from a building to allow evacuation in the event of a fire. (12 marks)
   (Total: 20 marks)

Model Answers

Short Questions

1. The three components of the fire triangle are:
   - Air - oxygen is necessary for combustion.
   - Heat - causes ignition.
   - Fuel - material, e.g. gas, that will burn.

2. The four classes of fire are as follows:
   - Class A - combustible materials.
   - Class B - fires involving liquids.
   - Class C - fires involving gases.
   - Class D - metal fires, e.g. aluminium or sodium.
   - Class F - fires fuelled by cooking fats, e.g. chip-pan fires.

   (Only four classes of fire are required.)

3. (a) A water extinguisher would be suitable for Class A fires (combustible materials).

   (b) A foam extinguisher would be suitable for:

   – Class B fires (liquids).
   – Class C fires (liquefied or petroleum gases).

   (c) A CO_2 extinguisher would be suitable for electrical fires. (This is not a separate class of fire.)

   (d) On flammable metals, a powder extinguisher could be used.

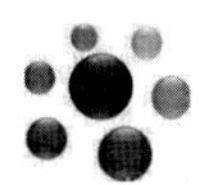

4. The four main methods of heat transfer are:

   - Direct burning: direct contact between the burning material and adjacent fuel sources.
   - Conduction: where heat is transferred through a conducting material (e.g. metal), without the conductor itself burning.
   - Convection: as the hot air and gases rise from the fire, cooler air is drawn in which, in turn, is heated and rises. The rising hot air gradually cools, spreads and descends. This continuous process of air being drawn in and heated, then rising, cooling and descending, forms circulating currents which enable the fire to spread.
   - Radiation: heat energy from the fire, in the form of infrared radiation, is transmitted through the air and may be absorbed by other fuel sources causing them to heat up, possibly enough to cause ignition.

5. When storing flammable liquids inside a building:

   - The stores should not be used to store other materials.
   - Flammable liquids should be separated from flammable gases.
   - Oxygen cylinders should be kept separate from flammable liquids.
   - The stores should be well ventilated.
   - Construction should be of fireproof materials.

   When flammable liquids are stored outside:

   - The stores should be at least three metres from any buildings.
   - Where a store is fenced off, the minimum height for the fence is 1.8 metres.
   - The stores should have at least two egress points.
   - The stores should be clearly marked.
   - Electrical fittings must be intrinsically safe.

Long Question

6. (a) Fire is spread by:

   - Convection.
   - Conduction.
   - Radiation.
   - Direct burning.

   (See answer to Question 4.)

   (b) Safe means of escape from a building requires:

   - Fire-resistance of walls and doors.
   - Fire compartments.
   - Protected stairways.
   - Emergency lighting.
   - Evacuation signs.
   - No obstructions.
   - Doors opening in the direction of travel.
   - A safe assembly point.
   - Training and awareness.
   - Means of raising the alarm.

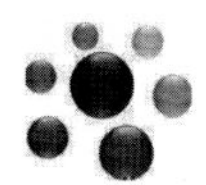

Element 8: Chemical and Biological Health Hazards and Risk Control

Forms, Classification and Health Risks from Exposure to Hazardous Substances

- **Chemical Agents**

  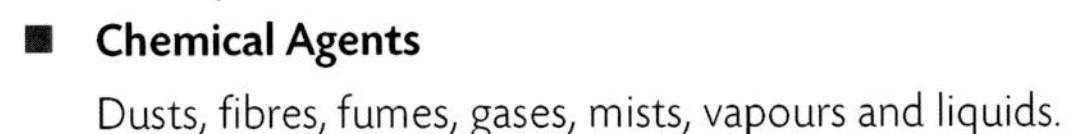

  Dusts, fibres, fumes, gases, mists, vapours and liquids.

- **Biological Agents**

  Fungi, bacteria and viruses.

Health Hazard Classifications

The *Globally Harmonised System of Classification and Labelling of Chemicals* (GHS) is a single internationally agreed system of chemical classification and hazard communication using labelling and Safety Data Sheets (SDS).

It includes harmonised criteria for the classification of:

- Physical hazards, e.g. explosive, oxidising, highly flammable.
- Health hazards, e.g. toxic, harmful, irritant, carcinogenic.
- Environmental hazards, e.g. harmful to aquatic organisms, dangerous for the ozone layer.

Criteria for classifying chemicals have been developed for the following GHS health hazard classes:

- Acute toxicity
- Skin corrosion/irritation
- Serious eye damage/eye irritation
- Respiratory or skin sensitisation
- Germ cell mutagenicity
- Carcinogenicity
- Reproductive toxicity
- Specific target organ toxicity (single and repeated exposure)
- Aspiration hazard.

The main classifications of chemicals hazardous to health may be summarised as follows:

- **Very toxic** or **toxic** substances and preparations cause death or acute or chronic damage to health when inhaled, swallowed or absorbed via the skin, even in small quantities.
- **Harmful** substances may cause death or acute or chronic damage to health when inhaled, swallowed or absorbed through the skin.
- **Corrosive** substances and preparations may destroy living tissues on contact and include:
  - **Acids** - sulphuric acid and hydrochloric acid in chemical cleaners, e.g. for masonry, brickwork.
  - **Alkalis** - cement, lime or agents used as chemical cleaners.
- **Irritant** substances and preparations are non-corrosive but may cause inflammation through immediate, prolonged or repeated contact with the skin or mucous membrane.
- **Carcinogenic** substances and preparations may induce cancer or increase its incidence if inhaled or ingested or absorbed by the skin.

Acute and Chronic Health Effects

- **Acute** health effects arise where the quantity of a toxic or harmful substance absorbed into the body produces harmful effects **very quickly**.
- **Chronic** health effects describe a condition where the harmful effects of a substance absorbed into the body take a **very long time** to appear - months or perhaps years.

Assessment of Health Risks

Routes of Entry

- **Inhalation** - entry is through the nose or mouth and along the respiratory passages to the lungs. The lung is the most vulnerable part of the body, as it can readily absorb gases, fumes, soluble dusts, mists and vapours. This is the main means of entry of biological agents.
- **Ingestion** - entry is by mouth and along the whole length of the gastrointestinal tract through the stomach, small and large bowel. Contamination may occur due to swallowing the agent directly, from eating or drinking contaminated foods or from eating with contaminated fingers. All forms of chemicals may be ingested, as can some biological agents.
- **Absorption** - entry is through the skin or eyes, through direct contact and with contaminated surfaces or from clothing.

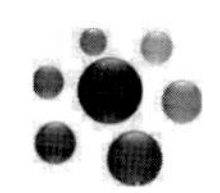

- **Aspiration** - a process whereby liquids or solids go directly into the lungs, other than by direct inhalation.
- **Injection** - entry is directly into the body by high-pressure equipment or contaminated sharp objects piercing the skin.

Defence Mechanisms

The body's response against the invasion of substances likely to cause damage can be divided into superficial and cellular defence mechanisms:

- **Superficial** - e.g. the "sneeze" reflex, nasal cavity filters and ciliary escalator.
- **Cellular** - e.g. macrophages, inflammatory response and prevention of excessive blood loss.

Assessing Health Risks

Where construction workers may be exposed to hazardous substances, it is necessary to assess the potential for harm to ensure it does not occur. This is a requirement of the **Control Of Substances Hazardous to Health Regulations 2002 (COSHH)** and the assessment is known as a "COSHH Assessment".

There are five steps to **COSHH** assessment:

1. Gather information about the substance used, the people who might be exposed and the work activities carried out.
2. Evaluate the health risks - are current controls adequate?
3. Identify any further controls and implement them.
4. Record the risk assessment and actions taken.
5. Review and revise.

Factors to consider when carrying out an assessment of health risks include:

- **Hazardous nature** of the substance - is it toxic, harmful, carcinogenic?
- **Physical form** of the substance - is it a solid, liquid, vapour or dust?
- The **quantity** of the hazardous substance present on site - including total amounts stored and the amounts actually in use or being created at any one time.
- Potential **ill-health effects** - will it cause minor ill health or very serious disease? And will this result from short-term or long-term exposure?
- **Duration** - how much exposure and for how long? Will it be for just a few minutes, or last all day?
- **Routes of entry** - will it be inhaled, swallowed, absorbed?
- **Concentration** - will a substance be used neat or diluted? What is the concentration in the air?
- The **number of people** potentially exposed and any vulnerable groups or individuals - such as expectant mothers or the infirm.
- The **control measures** that are already in place - such as ventilation systems and PPE.

Sources of Information

- **Product Labels**

  Under the **Chemicals (Hazard Information and Packaging for Supply) Regulations 2009 (CHIP 4)** suppliers of substances and preparations must inform users of the name of the substance (or, in the case of a preparation, the hazardous constituents) and indicate the level of danger by means of symbols on the labels.

- **HSE Guidance Note EH40**

  Guidance Note EH40 is the prime source of information about airborne contaminants. It contains the lists of **workplace exposure limits** for use with the **COSHH Regulations**.

- **Manufacturers' Safety Data Sheets**

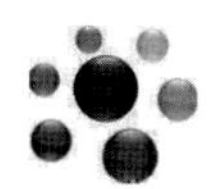

REACH requires suppliers of dangerous substances to provide sufficient information about the toxic effects and exposure limits of chemicals so that users can take appropriate workplace safety precautions in terms of use, transport and disposal. Data sheets and labels only provide general information that does not allow for localised conditions which might affect the risk.

Safety data sheets should contain the following information:

- Identification of the substance and supplier.
- Composition of substance.
- Hazard identification.
- First-aid measures.
- Accidental release measures.
- Fire-fighting measures.
- Handling and storage arrangements.
- Exposure control measures, including use of PPE.
- Physical and chemical properties.
- Stability and reactivity.
- Toxicological information.
- Ecological information.
- Disposal considerations.
- Transport information.
- Regulatory information.

From this information the employer must assess the risks of working with hazardous substances and ensure that appropriate control measures are in place to eliminate or minimise the risks from hazardous substances.

Limitations of Information in Assessing Risks to Health

Product labels, safety data sheets and WELs (EH40) provide detailed information about hazards and risks associated with a wide variety of hazardous substances. Risk assessment is the basis for determining control measures. It needs to be complemented by further information about the nature of the work and working practices before any evaluation is made about the risks to health posed by substances used at work.

Remember that product labels, safety data sheets and WELs are general statements not allowing for localised conditions in which substances are used.

Role and Limitations of Hazardous Substance Monitoring

Hazardous substance monitoring measures how much of a contaminant is in the air and we use this, together with time exposure, to assess the risks to health.

Sampling Techniques

Monitoring air quality involves:

- Collecting air samples either by a **spot** or **grab method** (i.e. single sample collected at a particular location) or by a **continuous monitored method** over a period of time.
- Identifying contaminants in the sample using **qualitative** (i.e. to determine constituents) or **quantitative analysis** (i.e. to determine levels of a particular agent).

Basic Monitoring Methods

- By diffusion or passive sampling using:
  - **Passive samplers** - versatile and easy to use for spot and continuous samples, they do not give immediate readings.
  - **Smoke tubes** - give general information about air flow or leaks in industrial equipment but can give unreliable readings and do not account for particle size of contaminants.
- By mechanical or active sampling using:
  - **Stain tube detectors** - simple to use, they pump air into a tube and give a direct reading of the concentration of the contaminant to be measured. You need to know what the contaminant is, as tubes are specific to a particular contaminant and can be affected by other substances present. Accuracy is limited to +/-25%.

Workplace Exposure Limits (WELs)

Workplace exposure limits (WELs) are maximum concentrations of airborne contaminants to which employees may be exposed (normally measured across a particular reference period of time).

They are found in HSE Guidance Note EH40 and define standards for acceptable air quality in terms of the amount of a particular substance in the atmosphere. Monitoring should ensure that the limits are not exceeded.

The main units used for measuring airborne concentrations are:

- Parts per million (ppm).
- Milligrams per cubic metre of air (mg/m^3, or $mg\ m^{-3}$).
- Fibres per millilitre of air (fibres ml^{-1}).

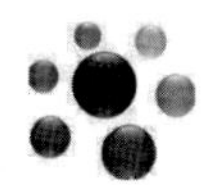

Long-Term and Short-Term Limits

- **Long-Term Exposure Limit**

  Level of airborne contaminant allowable over an 8-hour period, used for substances producing chronic effects.

- **Short-Term Exposure Limit**

  Level of airborne contaminant allowable over a 15-minute period, used for substances producing acute effects.

Limitations of Exposure Limits

WELs provide a general basis on which to assess what may be a safe level of concentration of airborne contamination but take no account of individual susceptibility or synergistic effects of mixtures of substances, and do not provide a definition between 'safe' and 'dangerous' conditions.

Principle of Reducing Exposure Levels

Reducing the workplace exposure to the contaminant controls risk. **COSHH** requires exposure to harmful substances be reduced to the lowest level reasonably practicable.

In practice, reducing exposure may mean more than simple compliance with the WEL. Under **COSHH**, if it is reasonably practicable to get contamination levels even lower, then that standard should be achieved. This is particularly important for controlling risk for certain groups such as asbestos and other carcinogens because there is no known safe dose.

Control Measures

Duty to Prevent Exposure

Under the **MHSWR** and **COSHH** the general hierarchy of control is to:

- Eliminate or substitute the hazard by using a less hazardous agent.
- Change the process, i.e. vacuum instead of brush.
- Reduce the time of exposure by providing regular breaks.
- Use physical or engineering controls to reduce the risk at source and provide general protection (segregation, enclosure, ventilation).
- Manage the task or person by job design and provide (as a last resort) personal protective equipment.

COSHH requires prevention or control of exposure to hazardous substances. If it is not reasonably practicable then the employer must:

- Change the process/activity to avoid its use or generation.
- Replace with a safer alternative.

- Use a safer form of substance.

Adequately Control Exposure

If prevention is not reasonably practicable, exposure is to be **adequately controlled**. Under **COSHH**, adequate control means:

- Apply the **eight principles of good practice** (Schedule 2A of **COSHH**).
- Not to exceed the WEL (if there is one).
- If substance causes cancer, heritable genetic damage or asthma, exposure must be reduced to as low as reasonably practicable (ALARP).

Ensuring WELs are Not Exceeded

WELs are established for a number of substances hazardous to health. The intention is to prevent excessive exposure by containing exposure below set limits. Application of the principles of good practice controls exposure to below the WEL.

The Principles of Good Practice

- **Principle 1** - design and operate processes and activities to minimise emission, release and spread of substances hazardous to health.
- **Principle 2** - take into account all relevant routes of exposure - inhalation, skin and ingestion - when developing control measures.
- **Principle 3** - control exposure by measures that are proportional to the health risk.
- **Principle 4** - choose the most effective and reliable control options that minimise the escape and spread of substances hazardous to health.
- **Principle 5** - where adequate control of exposure cannot be achieved by other means, provide, in combination with other control measures, suitable PPE.
- **Principle 6** - check and review regularly all elements of control measures for their continuing effectiveness.
- **Principle 7** - inform and train all employees on the hazards and risks from substances with which they work, and the use of control measures developed to minimise the risks.
- **Principle 8** - ensure that the introduction of measures to control exposure does not increase the overall risk to health and safety.

Control Measures Used to Implement the Principles of Good Practice

The **COSHH** hierarchy:

- **Elimination** or **substitution** of the hazardous substance.
- **Process changes.**

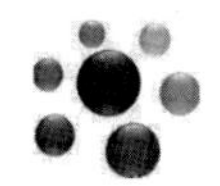

- **Reduced time exposure**, e.g. regular breaks/job rotation.
- **Enclosure and segregation** - enclosure may be total (glove boxes); partial (fume cupboards); movable (captor hoods) or directional (receptor hoods).
- **Local Exhaust Ventilation (LEV)** - the standard control measure for dealing with dusts, vapours and fumes generated at a particular point. Includes glove boxes, fume cupboards, captor hoods and receptor hoods and should be subject to regular visual inspection, planned preventive maintenance and periodic testing.
- **Dilution ventilation** - changes the air and dilutes the contaminant concentration using extraction fans, can be active or passive. Only appropriate for low hazard contaminants created at low rates, and which do not significantly enter the breathing zone of workers.
- **PPE** - used as a last resort. Includes:
  - Respiratory Protective Equipment (RPE):
  - Face mask - for dusts and fumes.
  - Half-face respirator - fits over the nose and mouth and has a removable canister.
  - Full-face respirator - fits over whole head/shoulders; air is pump-fed.
  - Air-fed respirator - fed by airline connected to mains air supply.
  - Self-contained breathing apparatus - supplied by canister of air worn by operative.
  - Other protective equipment and clothing:
  - Gloves, overalls, eye protection, safety helmets and safety footwear.

  When selecting PPE, a full risk assessment should be carried out to assess the suitability of the equipment supplied and identify any risk.

Personal Hygiene and Protection Regimes

Good welfare facilities for disinfection should be provided. Vaccinations may be required if warranted by a risk assessment.

Health Surveillance and Biological Monitoring

Where employees work with hazardous substances, risk assessment will identify whether health surveillance or biological monitoring is required.

The objectives of health surveillance with regard to hazardous substances are:

- To protect employees' health by detection, as soon as possible, of any signs of ill-health connected with the work process.
- To assist in the evaluation of control measures.
- To collect and evaluate data and statistics, and to ensure effective controls.
- To educate employees and make them aware of the need for health surveillance.

Other functions include:

- Pre-employment health screening to ensure that there is no reason why someone should not work with hazardous substances.
- Biological monitoring, e.g. blood tests, urine tests, chest X-rays, lung function - any of these tests may be appropriate for employees working with hazardous substances.

Further Controls for Carcinogens, Asthmagens and Mutagens

COSHH requires that exposure to substances that can cause cancer, asthma or damage to genes should be prevented. If this is not possible, a hierarchy of controls is to be adopted:

- Total enclosure of the process and handling systems.
- Prohibition of eating, drinking and smoking in contaminated areas.
- Regular cleaning of floors, walls and other surfaces.
- Designation of areas that may be contaminated with warning signs.
- Safe storage, handling and disposal.

Specific Agents

Agent	Source Materials	Route of Entry	Main Health Effects
Petro-chemicals	Petrol, diesel and oils used in machinery.	Skin contact.	Defatting, dermatitis.
Organic Solvents	Corrosive chemicals found in paints (butanol), varnishes, solvents (toluene, xylene), pesticides, etc.	Absorption or inhalation of vapours.	Skin and eye irritation and inflammation; also dermatitis, burns, drowsiness and nausea.
Carbon Dioxide (CO_2)	Smoke from incinerators; also in its solid form (freezing point).	Inhalation.	Asphyxia; breathlessness and loss of consciousness.
Nitrogen (N)	Diesel emissions, use of explosives, use of inerting gas.	Inhalation	Asphyxia; breathlessness and loss of consciousness.
Carbon Monoxide (CO)	Colourless, tasteless gas found in coal gas, car exhaust, blast furnace gas.	Inhalation.	Loss of consciousness and death over time.
Isocyanates	Adhesives, synthetic rubber, polyurethane paints and lacquers.	Inhalation of vapours.	Inflammation of nose and throat membranes. Chronic asthma.

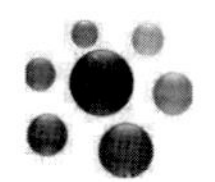

Lead - inorganic and organic compounds	Lead/acid car batteries and pigments; building processes (plumbing; welding).	Inhalation of lead dust or by inhalation and skin contact for organic lead compounds.	Nausea, vomiting and headaches; disorders of the blood and nervous systems (weakness and insomnia).
Asbestos	As a heat and electricity insulator (lagging and roofing), or brake linings.	Inhalation of fibres.	Respiratory diseases and lung cancers (i.e. asbestosis; mesothelioma).
Silica	Sandstone, quartz and slate.	Inhalation of dust.	Chest and respiratory diseases; collagenous and non-collagenous pneumoconiosis.
Cement Dust, Wet Cement	Building materials - mortar, plaster and concrete.	Mainly by skin contact, inhalation of dust, and manual handling.	Dermatitis and burns.
Wood Dust	Wood dust, and the resins, stains and wood preservatives	Skin contact and inhalation. Ingestion.	Skin disorders; conjunctivitis; coughing and asthma; nasal cancer; stomach problems (ingestion).
Leptospira	Rats.	Absorption through skin.	Weil's disease - fever; liver disease.
Legionella	Water, sludge or organic materials in cooling towers and condensers/ humidifiers.	Inhalation.	Legionnaires' disease and Pontiac fever.
Hepatitis	From sewage (sewers or contaminated land), contaminated sharps, or directly from sick people.	Injection or ingestion.	Fever, jaundice, enlargement of the liver, haemorrhages.
Tetanus	Contaminated soil; vegetation; splinters.	Open skin wounds.	"Lock jaw". Muscular spasm and respiratory problems.
HIV/AIDA	Infected Blood borne	Occupationally - through absorption/ through open skin wounds or injection through skin	Compromised immune system.
Hydrogen Sulphide	Gas occurs naturally in volcanoes, hot springs, etc. Industrial production at refineries, tanneries, paper mills, etc.	Inhalation	Chemical asphyxiation.

Generation and Control of Dusts on a Construction Site

- **Silica**

  Silica is a known carcinogen and while the WEL of 0.1 mg/m^3 for Respirable Crystalline Silica (RCS) must not be exceeded, levels should be kept as low as reasonably practicable.

  Specific precautions should be employed, e.g. assessment, elimination or substitution, dust control, PPE, welfare facilities and health surveillance.

- **Fibres (MMMF)**

  PPE can only be used if it is not reasonably practicable to use other measures, e.g. local exhaust ventilation.

  General precautionary measures might not apply in all circumstances and should be adapted for local conditions.

  Perhaps a substitute, non-fibrous material can be used.

  Dust suppressants, non-fibrous bonding materials or coating the product with a protective sealant should be considered. Precautions should include: engineering controls, work planning/housekeeping and PPE.

- **Asbestos**

  Work with asbestos in the workplace is covered by the **Control of Asbestos Regulations 2012**.

  Asbestos controls include restricting access and sealing off the area, testing the sealed area for leaks, providing appropriate protective equipment (coveralls, respirators) and a decontamination unit. There should be thorough cleaning of the area and a clean air certificate obtained on successful completion.

- **Cement Dust**

  Elimination or substitution should be the first step to prevent contact with cement. Otherwise, control measures minimising skin contact should be applied. Good washing facilities, use of gloves, PPE and health surveillance should be used.

- **Wood Dust**

  Hard and soft wood dusts have WELs of 5mg/m^3 and must not be exceeded. Wood dust is an asthmagen. Exposure must be reduced as low as is reasonably practicable.

  Key controls are: LEV and a collection system, clearance of wood dust with a vacuum system. RPE should additionally be used for very dusty tasks. Asthma can be averted with good health surveillance.

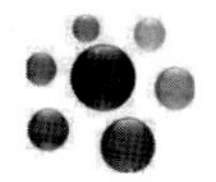

Health Risks and Controls Associated with Asbestos

The main regulations governing all work with asbestos on workplace premises are the **Control of Asbestos Regulations 2012**. The Regulations prohibit the importation, supply and use of all forms of asbestos and include a duty to manage asbestos. (Note: existing asbestos-containing materials in good condition do not have to be removed but must be monitored and managed.)

Three respiratory diseases are associated with asbestos exposure:

- Asbestosis.
- Lung cancer.
- Mesothelioma.

Duty to Manage Asbestos

Identification is essential for asbestos management. Samples should be sent to a lab for testing to identify types of asbestos present.

Surveys should be carried out to:

- Locate materials assumed to contain asbestos and note what condition they are in.
- Take and analyse samples to confirm whether asbestos is present. This is done only by a qualified asbestos specialist.
- Get full access to all parts of the building, using destructive inspection if necessary to locate asbestos. Usually used just before demolition or major refurbishment. Only done by a qualified asbestos specialist.

The results of all types of survey should be recorded and the information provided to anyone who may work on, or disturb, these materials. Safety representatives are entitled to this information.

Asbestos can be found in construction materials including:

- Insulation board.
- Pipe lagging.
- Fire blankets.
- Floor tiles.
- Sprayed coatings/loose fill.
- Roof felt.

- Decorative paints and plasters.
- Asbestos cement products, including:
  - Corrugated roof sheets.
  - Rainwater goods (fountain heads, guttering, drain pipes, etc.).
  - Cold water tanks and toilet cisterns.

Procedures must be put in place for the **discovery of asbestos**, whether discovered during investigation or accidentally.

Accidental Exposure to Asbestos

- Stop work immediately.
- Prevent anyone entering the area.
- Arrangements should be made to contain the asbestos - seal the area.
- Put up warning signs - 'possible asbestos contamination'.
- Inform the site supervisor immediately.
- If contaminated, all clothing, equipment, etc. should be decontaminated and disposed of as hazardous waste.
- Undress, shower, wash hair; put on clean clothes.
- Contact a specialist surveyor or asbestos removal contractor.

Safe removal should be carried out **under license** as required.

If the work is licensable, advance notice to the enforcing authority is to be given. The notification (as per Schedule 1 of the 2012 Regulations) should contain:

- The name, address and telephone number of the notifier.
- Location of the work site.
- A description of the type of asbestos to be removed or handled.
- The maximum quantity of asbestos to be held on the premises.
- The activities or processes involved.
- The number of workers involved.
- Measures taken to limit the exposure of employees to asbestos.
- Date of commencement and expected duration of work activity.

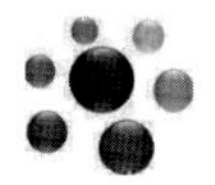

Plan of Work

Before work begins, a **written plan** detailing how work is to be carried out must be provided. It should specify control measures required for managing risk, including:

- Monitoring the condition of any asbestos or ACMs.
- Ensuring asbestos or ACMs are maintained or safely removed.
- Providing information about the location and condition of any asbestos or ACMs to anyone liable to disturb it/them.
- Making this information available to the emergency services.

The measures specified in the plan must be implemented and recorded and the plan should be reviewed and revised as required.

Control Measures

The control measures for work with asbestos include:

- Restrict access to the area.
- Enclose the work area and keep it under negative pressure, testing for leaks.
- Provide appropriate PPE and a decontamination unit.
- Ensure removal operatives are suitably trained.
- Use controlled wet removal methods. Dry removal processes are unacceptable.
- Use a wrap-and-cut method or glove bag technique.
- Where appropriate, use measures which control the fibres at source. Failing this, use equipment hand-held by a second employee next to the source emitting the fibres.
- Thoroughly clean the area and obtain a clean air certificate upon completion of the work.

A clearance certificate for reoccupation may only be issued by the United Kingdom Accreditation Service (UKAS).

Respiratory Equipment

- Suitable RPE should always be provided where exposure can be above the control limits; it must be marked with a 'CE' symbol and matched to the exposure concentrations, job, wearer and factors related to the working environment.
- RPE must be examined and tested at suitable intervals by a competent person, and a suitable record kept for five years. Respirator testing involves daily checks, monthly checks, and full performance checks every six months.
- Operator checks would involve fit testing to see that the correct size and model are used to provide an adequate face seal.

Protective Clothing

- **Overalls** - disposable (hooded) overalls are suitable. Waterproof overalls for outdoor work. Never take used overalls home.
- **Gloves** - if worn, use single-use disposable gloves. If latex, choose 'low-protein powder' gloves. Dispose of as asbestos waste.
- **Footwear** - boots are preferable to disposable overshoes. Never use laced boots - they have lace holes to catch asbestos fibres and are difficult to clean.

Information, Instruction and Training

Anyone removing asbestos must have training that includes:

- Properties of asbestos and its effects on health.
- Products or materials likely to contain asbestos.
- Operations which could result in asbestos exposure.
- Safe work practices, preventive control measures, and protective equipment.
- Purpose, choice, limitations, proper use and maintenance of RPE.
- Emergency procedures and hygiene requirements.
- Decontamination and waste handling procedures.
- **Medical** examination requirements:

  Surveillance for persons who are exposed to asbestos requires:

  - A health record is kept (for 40 years) and maintained.
  - Medical surveillance by a doctor where exposure exceeds the action level. A certificate of medical examination for asbestos should be kept for four years.
- The control limit and the need for **air monitoring**:

  Sampling for asbestos in the air should be carried out by trained staff, in three situations:

  - Compliance sampling - within control or action limits.
  - Background sampling - before starting work (i.e. removal).
  - Clearance sampling - after removal and cleaning the area.

Employees should be made aware of the significant findings of the risk assessment, and the results of any air monitoring carried out, with an explanation of the findings.

Requirements for Disposal

Every employer who undertakes work with asbestos must ensure that raw asbestos or asbestos waste is labelled in accordance with the provisions of the regulations and disposed of by landfill that can accept asbestos.

Safe Handling and Storage of Waste

The main legislation relating to environmental protection and management is the **Environmental Protection Act 1990**.

Duty of Care

The duty of care is applicable to all persons involved in the generation, importation, handling, transporting and disposal of controlled waste and places a responsibility on them to ensure that waste:

- Is managed legally and does not escape from control.
- Is transferred only to an authorised person.
- Is adequately described.
- Is accompanied by appropriate documentation, i.e. a Transfer Note.

Hazardous Waste

- **Hazardous waste** is generally waste that is highly flammable, toxic, carcinogenic, corrosive, etc.
- **Non-hazardous waste** generally includes household waste, paper, wood and other biodegradable materials.

The **Hazardous Waste (England and Wales) Regulations 2005** and the **List of Wastes (England) Regulations 2005** require that:

- Hazardous waste producers **identify** when their waste is hazardous.
- Premises that produce or hold hazardous waste (>500kg per annum) are **registered** with the Environment Agency (EA)/Natural Resources Wales (NRW).
- A **Consignment Note** is completed when any hazardous waste is moved from premises and all receivers of hazardous waste submit a quarterly **Consignee Return** to the EA.

Safe Handling and Storage

Factors to consider when assessing management of waste in workplaces include:

- The **hazardous nature** of the waste - may require the use of PPE.
- Any **manual handling** risk that may be presented - may require mechanical handling equipment or handling aids.
- Storage equipment such as skips, bins and compactors may be difficult to **access** - may require steps or platforms to allow safe use.
- Compactors will have **moving parts** - should be effectively guarded.
- Collection **vehicles** such as skip lorries present a significant hazard when manoeuvring - should be seen back by a banksman.
- The waste may present a temptation to scavengers and vandals - must be **secured**.
- Any escape may have the potential to cause **pollution** - waste securing might control this risk. Emergency spill or release plans may also be required.
- Waste types (streams) - must be **segregated**. Requires separate secure storage for each type of waste and clear identification of types.
- Appropriate **documentation** should accompany the waste and the duty of care must be fulfilled.

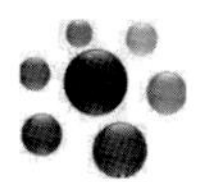

Exam-Style Questions

Short Questions

1. **Identify EIGHT** possible physical forms of hazardous substances that workers might potentially encounter at work. (8 marks)

2. **Outline** the difference between acute and chronic exposure to hazardous substances, and how these exposures have different effects on the body. (8 marks)

3. Legionellosis (Legionnaires' disease) is a disease caused by *legionella* bacteria entering water supplies. **Describe FOUR** workplace sources where people could be exposed to *legionella* bacteria that have entered a water supply. (8 marks)

4. A construction company had noticed a recent increase in work-related ill health amongst site workers who use a degreasing solvent for which a Workplace Exposure Limit (WEL) has been assigned.
   (a) **Explain** the meaning of the term 'Workplace Exposure Limit (WEL)'. (2 marks)
   (b) **Give** reasons for the possible increase in work-related ill health amongst construction site workers who are using the solvent. (6 marks)

   (Total: 8 marks)

5. The manufacturer/supplier of a hazardous chemical has to prepare a safety data sheet for the chemical. **Identify EIGHT** topic headings for the information that should be included on a safety data sheet. (8 marks)

Long Question

6. (a) **Explain**, with examples, the main routes of entry into the body that a hazardous substance might take. (8 marks)
   (b) **Outline** the main classification categories that can be assigned to hazardous substances and **give** an example of a specific chemical or substance for each classification category. (12 marks)

   (Total: 20 marks)

Model Answers

Short Questions

1. The possible physical forms of a hazardous substance are:
   - Liquid.
   - Gas.
   - Vapour.
   - Mist.
   - Fume.
   - Dust.
   - Aerosol.
   - Solid.
   - Granules.

   (Only eight are required.)

2. When working with hazardous substances:
   - An acute exposure arises very quickly with harmful effects and can be seen within minutes of exposure.
   - A chronic exposure takes a long time to become apparent (months or years); usually results from absorption of small quantities over a period of time.

3. *Legionella* could occur in the following workplace situations:
   - Cooling towers.
   - Evaporative condensers.
   - Hot/cold water services where people are susceptible, e.g. health care.
   - Humidifiers and air washers.
   - Spa baths and pools.

   (Only four are required.)

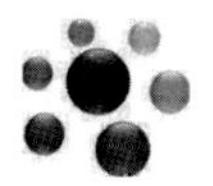

4. (a) A WEL is the maximum concentration of an airborne contaminant, averaged over a reference period (15 minutes or eight hours), to which employees may be exposed by inhalation.

   (b) Reasons include:

   - Inadequacy of the original risk assessment - increase in frequency and duration of exposure to employees compared to the original assessment; the degreasing solvent currently used may be different from the one used when the original assessment was conducted.
   - New employees - failure to carry out health screening and to give training on hazards and precautions, etc.
   - WEL exceeded - poor maintenance of the LEV and failure to carry out monitoring to ensure that the WEL is not exceeded.

5. A safety data sheet should contain the following topics:

   - Substance identification.
   - Supplier.
   - Composition.
   - Identification of hazards.
   - Risk phrases.
   - Safety phrases - toxicological information.
   - First-aid measures - ecological information.
   - Fire-fighting measures - disposal information.
   - Transport information - spillage measures.
   - Handling and storage.
   - PPE requirements.
   - Stability.

   (Only eight are required.)

Long Question

6. (a) A hazardous substance may enter the body by the following routes:

   - Injection, e.g. a contaminated needle.
   - Inhalation, e.g. of fumes.
   - Ingestion, e.g. due to poor personal hygiene.
   - Absorption, e.g. of a chemical liquid.

   (b) The main classification categories of hazardous substance are:

   - Harmful, e.g. solvents in paint.
   - Irritant, e.g. ammonia.
   - Corrosive, e.g. sulphuric acid.
   - Toxic, e.g. carbon monoxide.
   - Very toxic, e.g. chlorine.
   - Sensitising, e.g. isocyanates.
   - Carcinogenic, e.g. asbestos.

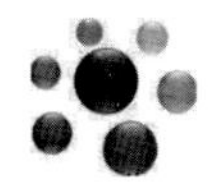

Element 9: Physical and Psychological Health Hazards and Risk Control

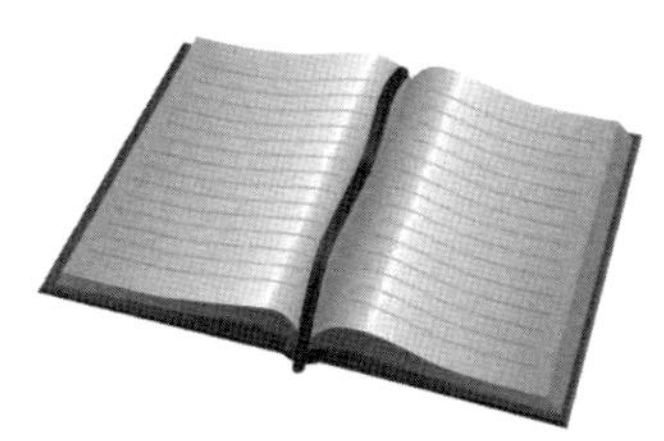

Noise

The **Control of Noise at Work Regulations 2005** provide a framework for assessing and regulating noise levels at work.

Physical and Psychological Effects on Hearing of Exposure to Noise

Exposure to excessive levels of noise can cause temporary, and permanent, hearing loss. This is usually gradual and is caused by prolonged exposure, sometimes over many years. However, permanent hearing damage can also be caused by a sudden single exposure to a very loud noise (peak sound pressure). This form of hearing damage is less common, examples include gunfire, explosion or other instantaneous or percussive type noise sources.

Additionally, exposure to excessive levels of noise can cause tinnitus (a ringing, whistling or buzzing in the ears).

Noise may also affect concentration and the irritation can lead to stress effects.

Generally, the effects of permanent hearing damage are irreversible.

Assessment of Exposure

Noise is measured in decibels.

Because the human ear detects both frequency and pressure, we need to take account of this when we measure average noise levels, so a filter known as 'A weighting' (dB(A)), is built into the calculation. This 'A weighting' filter mimics the responses of the human ear to sound.

When measuring peak sound pressure, e.g. instantaneous 'explosive' type noise, a 'C weighting' filter (dB(C)) is used.

The damaging effects of noise are related to the total amount of energy or 'dose' which the ear receives. The dose/energy depends on two factors - the level of noise and duration of exposure. This personal noise exposure is usually written as $L_{EP,d}$ (daily) or $L_{EP,w}$ (weekly).

Exposure Action Values and Exposure Limit Values

These are exposure values at or above which the employer is required to take particular steps to protect employees and others from the harmful effects of noise.

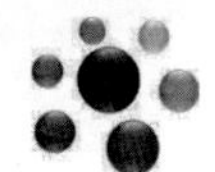

- **Lower Exposure Action Values**: 80 dB(A) $L_{EP,d}$ / $L_{EP,w}$ or 135 dB(C)

  Where it is likely that a lower exposure action value may be exceeded, employers must carry out a *risk assessment*.

  At or above this level employees must be provided with information about the likely noise exposure and the associated risk to hearing, the control measures in place to reduce exposure, hearing protection and health surveillance (hearing tests).

- **Upper Exposure Action Values**: 85 dB(A) $L_{EP,d}$ / $L_{EP,w}$ or 137 dB(C)

  At or above this level the employer must reduce exposure to as low a level as is reasonably practicable by establishing and implementing a programme of organisational and technical measures. The provision of hearing protectors is a last resort and is only acceptable when other methods of reducing exposure are not reasonably practicable.

  Health surveillance (hearing checks) must be provided for all employees likely to be exposed regularly above the upper exposure action value.

- **Exposure Limit Values**: 87 dB(A) $L_{EP,d}$ / $L_{EP,w}$ or 140 dB(C)

  These limits must not be exceeded. However, if an exposure limit value is exceeded, the employer must investigate the reason for the occurrence and identify and implement actions to ensure that it does not occur again.

Simple Noise Measurement Techniques

Personal noise exposure can be calculated from measurements obtained from a simple sound level meter when working in a single location and noise levels are constant. However, noise exposure is more difficult to measure where noise level is variable or workers' movements are irregular.

Noise dosimeters provide a simple means of measuring personal exposure where workers are exposed to complex and variable noise fields.

Basic Noise Control Measures

Wherever noise is a problem there are three orders of priority for dealing with it:

- **Noise reduction at source** - by **elimination** or **substitution** of the process or equipment producing the noise. (Source.)
- **Attenuation in transmission** using engineering controls which limit the amount of noise transmitted (i.e. isolation or segregation encloses the noise source; absorption or insulation reduces reverberation of noise; damping or silencing reduces vibration and sound). (Pathway.)
- **Personal protection** - hearing protection should be used only if neither of the first two approaches results in a satisfactory solution. (Receiver.)

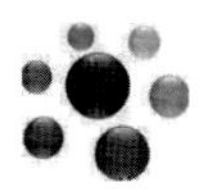

Personal Hearing Protection

- **Ear muffs or defenders** fit completely over the ears. There can be compatibility/fit problems when used with other PPE such as hard hats or safety glasses.
- **Ear plugs** fit in the ear canal. They need a degree of training and there are hygiene issues.

Hearing protection should be selected based on the attenuation (noise reduction) given by the hearing protection. Hearing protection used should be regularly monitored and maintained.

Role of Monitoring and Health Surveillance

Health surveillance is an important part of the hierarchy and involves regular checks on hearing in controlled conditions (audiometry). There should be consultation with trade union safety representatives or employee representatives before the surveillance programme commences.

Vibration

Effects on the Body of Exposure to Vibration

- **Hand-Arm Vibration Syndrome**

  Regular exposure to hand/arm vibration can cause a range of permanent injuries to hands and arms, collectively known as **Hand-Arm Vibration Syndrome** (**HAVS**).

  HAVS is a notifiable disease under the **Reporting of Injuries, Diseases and Dangerous Occurrences Regulations 2013**.

  Factors contributing to the effects include the level of vibration which reaches the limbs (**frequency**) and how long they are exposed to it (**duration**).

  Risk activities include use of all types of hammer tools and rotary equipment which can expose workers to high levels of hand/arm vibration, e.g. chainsaws, circular saws; hammer drills; hand-held grinders, particularly if operators are exposed for long periods in the day.

- **Whole Body Vibration**

  Whole Body Vibration (**WBV**) can result from using various construction vehicles or compactors, and possibly cause other injuries to the knees, hips and back.

Assessment of Exposure

The **Control of Vibration at Work Regulations (CVAWR) 2005** place duties on employers including:

- A requirement to assess the risks to their employees from vibration.
- Introduction of control measures whenever an Exposure Action Value (EAV) is exceeded.

- Ensuring workers are not exposed to vibration above a specific Exposure Limit Value (ELV).
- Notifying the employee of the risk.
- Giving information relating to the risk assessment, including the reporting of symptoms.
- Training in safe working practices.
- Beginning health surveillance.

Risk assessment should enable you to decide whether exposures is likely to be above the EAV or ELV and to identify which work activities need to be controlled.

The assessment must be completed by a competent person who must have had specific training, know the work processes being used and know how to collect and understand the relevant information.

Exposure Action Value and Exposure Limit Value

CVAWR require employers to take specific action when the daily vibration exposure reaches a certain action value.

- **Exposure action value** is a daily amount of vibration exposure above which employers are required to take action to control exposure.
  - For hand-arm vibration the EAV is a daily exposure of 2.5m/s2 A(8).
- **Exposure limit value** is the maximum amount of vibration an employee may be exposed to on any single day.
  - For hand-arm vibration the ELV is a daily exposure of 5m/s2 A(8). It represents a high risk above which employees should not be exposed.

Basic Vibration Control Measures

These can mainly be divided into the following groups:

- Class of equipment.
- Maintenance.
- Limiting exposure.
- Personal protective equipment.

Other controls may be available depending on the particular equipment and circumstances.

Role of Monitoring and Health Surveillance

Health surveillance should be conducted where appropriate, such as in cases where the risk assessment shows a risk of developing vibration-related conditions, or employees may be exposed at or above the exposure action values. Records should be kept. Where an identifiable disease related to vibration exposure is discovered, the employer needs to:

- Ensure that a qualified person informs the employee accordingly and provides the employee with information and advice.
- Ensure that he or she is informed of any significant findings.
- Review the risk assessment.
- Review any measures taken to control risk from vibration.
- Consider assigning the employee to alternative work where there is no risk from further exposure to vibration.
- Provide for a review of the health of any other employee who has been similarly exposed.

Radiation

Health Effects Associated with Radiation

There are basically two forms of radiation:

- **Ionising radiation** comes from alpha, beta, gamma-rays, X-rays, neutrons and radon. Exposure to this type of radiation can be acute or chronic; it can cause sickness, cancer or other cell destruction.
- **Non-ionising radiation** which can take the form of:
  - Ultraviolet radiation - can redden skin (sunburn) or cause eye inflammation (arc eye). Construction workers working outside are particularly at risk.
  - Visible radiation from high intensity beams such as lasers - can cause serious burns to exposed skin tissue, and is particularly dangerous to the eyes, e.g. printers and photocopiers in site offices.
  - Infrared radiation emitted from any hot material - can cause reddening of the skin, burns and cataracts in the eyes, e.g. molten glass, foundries, catering establishments.
  - Microwave radiation - can affect eyes and cause deep burns.
  - Radio frequency radiation - can cause excessive heating of exposed tissues near high-powered radio transmitter aerials, overhead power lines and mobile phone base stations.

Artificial optical radiation is not a form of radiation in itself, but includes many non-ionising sources. The **Control of Artificial Optical Radiation at Work Regulations (AOR) 2010** requires employers to consider controlling exposure to such artificial sources, to ensure they cause no harm.

Typical Occupational Sources of Radiation

- **Ionising Radiation**

Alpha particles	Smoke detectors and science labs.
Beta particles	Science labs and thickness gauges.
X-rays	Medical radiography, baggage security scanners, non-destructive testing of equipment and machinery.
Gamma rays	Industrial radiography.
Neutrons	Nuclear power stations.
Radon	A naturally occurring radioactive gas originating from uranium which occurs naturally in many rocks and soils.

- **Non-Ionising Radiation**

UV	Sunlight; arc-welding and oxy-fuel welding/burning. Curing of paint in manufacturing and vehicle painting processes. Curing of inks in printing.
Visible light	Laser levelling devices; laser pointer.
IR	Red-hot steel in a rolling mill; glass manufacture; ceramics (clay ware) manufacture.
Microwaves	Food processing (ovens); telecommunications equipment (mobile phone masts).
Radio waves	Radio, TV or radar transmitters.

Controlling Exposure to Radiation

Ionising Radiation

The **Ionising Radiations Regulations 1999 (IRR99)** provide the framework for controls which limit exposure to the absolute minimum by using time, distance and shielding:

- **Time** - minimise the duration of exposure.
- **Distance** - the dose will get lower the further away from the source you get. Alpha and beta rays behave differently to gamma and x-rays.
- **Shielding** - relatively thin shields can be used with alpha and beta particles, but X-rays and gamma rays

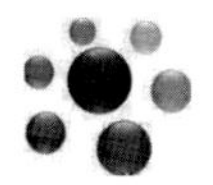

Non-Ionising Radiation

Control of exposure to non-ionising radiation is generally through the use of barriers (engineering controls) and PPE. However, prolonged exposure to ultraviolet radiation may need warning signs, access restrictions and limited exposure times. All require information, instruction and training.

Basic Radiation Protection Strategies

- A **Radiation Protection Adviser** (RPA) must be appointed where controlled areas have been designated. RPAs must have experience of the type of work the employer undertakes and be able to provide appropriate advice and guidance.
- **Local rules** - must be provided by employers to describe the safe systems of working with ionising radiation. These must be prominently displayed and brought to the attention of all relevant employees.

  One or more **Radiation Protection Supervisors** (RPSs) must be appointed (usually internally) to be responsible for enforcing the local rules.

Controlled and Supervised Areas

Where a radiation hazard is present, the area must be designated by the RPA and access restricted to classified workers. Two categories of area for radiation work are determined by the likely radiation dose of those working in the area:

- **Controlled area** - exposures exceeding three tenths of a dose limit may be received; includes where radioactive materials are stored and dispensed.
- **Supervised area** - exposures between one tenth and three tenths of a dose limit may be received; includes most areas in which work with radiation is carried out.

A **safe system of work** will include rules for handling radioactive source material, action in the event of accidents or other incidents, and procedures on leaving a controlled or supervised area. A formal **permit-to-work system** may be required to restrict time spent in the radiation area. Areas designated as controlled or supervised areas must have washing and changing facilities.

The Role of Monitoring and Health Surveillance

The International Commission on Radiological Protection (ICRP) has set the following dose limits on exposure to ionising radiation:

- The general public shall not be exposed to more than 1 mSv per year.
- Occupational exposure shall not exceed 20 mSv per year.

These limits exclude exposure due to background and medical radiation.

Three forms of monitoring are used:

- **Personal monitoring** - personal dosimeters used for those in controlled and supervised areas; may measure whole body dose or partial body dose (i.e. the fingers).
- **Medical examination** - routine examinations conducted before employment and every 12 months; immediate special examination after an over-exposure.
- **Area monitoring** - levels of radiation in controlled and supervised areas must be regularly assessed and monitoring equipment properly maintained, examined and tested.

Records of all monitoring must be kept.

Stress

Stress - the adverse reaction people have to excessive pressure or other types of demand placed on them.

Causes of Stress

- **Demand** - high and conflicting job demands as well as poor environmental working conditions.
- **Control** - poorly defined job duties or responsibilities, and lack of job security.
- **Support** - lack of training and support.
- **Relationships** - poor working relationships with supervisors, managers and peers, and harassment.
- **Role** - workers unsure of scope, responsibility and job requirements (ambiguity) or subjected to conflicting demand.
- **Change** - the introduction of new working conditions or processes without consultation or training.

Personal issues can also have a bearing.

Effects of Stress

Employee - the symptoms of stress may be physical or psychological. If intense stress is allowed to persist, it can lead to alcohol abuse and to serious physical and mental health conditions, such as high blood pressure, heart disease and depression.

Employer - stress is a major cause of sickness absence among employees, so it represents a significant cost to employers. It can also lead to low morale and high staff turnover.

Control Strategies

Case law emphasises the particular need to minimise stress, especially for an employee with a record of stress-related illness. The basic management framework should be based around the same issues listed as causes of stress:

- **Demands**
  - Should be reasonable and, where possible, set in consultation with workers.
  - Working hours and shift patterns should be carefully selected and flexible hours allowed where possible.
  - Workers should be selected on their competence, skills and ability to cope with difficult or demanding work.
- **Control**
  - Employees should be encouraged to have more say in how their work is carried out and how problems will be tackled.
- **Support**
  - Feedback to employees will improve performance and maintain motivation. All feedback should be positive and should focus on behaviour, not on personality.
  - Workers should have adequate training, information and instruction.
- **Relationships**
  - Clear standards of conduct should be communicated.
  - Policies in place to tackle misconduct, harassment and bullying.
- **Role**
  - Role should be defined by an up-to-date job description; clear work objectives; and reporting responsibilities.
  - If employees are uncertain about their job or the nature of a task, they should be encouraged to ask at an early stage.
- **Change**
  - If change has to take place, employees should be consulted about what the organisation wants to achieve and given the opportunity to comment, ask questions and get involved.
  - Employees should be supported before, during and after the change.

Exam-Style Questions

Short Questions

1. **Outline EIGHT** possible work-related causes of increased stress levels amongst employees. Ignore those that are associated with the physical environment at work. (8 marks)

2. **Outline** the employer's responsibilities, under the **Control of Noise at Work Regulations 2005**, when employee exposure to noise is at, or above, the lower exposure action value **AND** at, or above, the upper exposure action value. (8 marks)

3. Workers who use vibrating hand-held tools can suffer from several occupational diseases as a result of their hand-arm vibration exposure:
   (a) **Identify** the typical signs and symptoms that workers might experience if they are suffering from such diseases. (4 marks)
   (b) **Outline** the workplace precautions that may be used to minimise the risk of hand-arm vibration-related diseases. (4 marks)

   (Total: 8 marks)

4. (a) **Identify TWO** types of non-ionising radiation **AND** for **EACH** type **give** a specific example of a source that is related to construction work. (4 marks)

   (Total: 8 marks)

   (b) **Describe** the possible health effects that might follow on from exposure to non-ionising radiation. (4 marks)

Long Question

5. Workers carrying out maintenance work on plant on a construction site are required to clean machinery using high pressure compressed air. Noise levels have been measured at 95 dB(A).
   (a) **Explain** the meaning of the unit "dB(A)" as used in the sentence above. (2 marks)
   (b) **Outline** the control measures that should be considered in order to eliminate or reduce the risk of hearing damage **BOTH** to the maintenance staff **AND** to other site workers who have to work near to the maintenance activities. (10 marks)
   (c) **Outline** the factors that should be thought about when selecting suitable hearing protection for the task, and **identify** the limitations of such hearing protection. (8 marks)

   (Total: 20 marks)

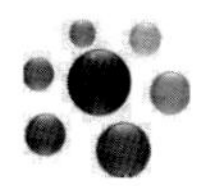

Model Answers

Short Questions

1. Possible causes of work-related increased stress levels are:
   - Shift work and unsocial hours.
   - Repetitive or monotonous work.
   - Lack of control over the job.
   - Workload too high or low.
   - Task or person mismatch.
   - Harassment, bullying and discrimination.
   - Fear of violence.
   - Poor relationships with colleagues.
   - Financial worries.

   (Only eight are required.)

2. At the **lower exposure action value**, the employer must:
   - Assess the noise, using a competent person.
   - Inform, instruct and train staff on the risks from noise exposure and the control measures to be used.
   - Make hearing protection available.

   At the **upper exposure action value**, the employer must:
   - Introduce a programme of measures to reduce exposure.
   - Provide ear defenders.
   - Provide signage to indicate noise areas.
   - Give information and training.
   - Ensure that PPE is worn.

3. (a) This answer requires only information regarding HAVS as the problem relates to hand-held tools, so references to WBV are irrelevant.

    Symptoms of Hand-Arm Vibration Syndrome (HAVS) include:

    - **Vibration white-finger** - the blood supply to the fingers shuts down and the fingers turn white, with the problem appearing to be worse in cold and wet conditions.
    - **Nerve damage** - the fingers suffer a loss of pressure, heat and pain sensitivity as the nerves to the fingers stop working properly.
    - **Muscle weakening** - grip strength and manual dexterity are reduced.
    - **Joint damage** - can cause abnormal bone growth to appear at finger joints.

   (b) Workplace precautions to reduce the risk of hand-arm vibration damage include:

    - Choose equipment carefully:
      - Mechanise where possible.
      - Change tools for those that vibrate less.
      - Support the tools.
      - Use anti-vibration mounts.
    - Maintain tools properly:
      - Lubricate moving parts.
      - Keep cutting tools sharp.
      - Replace vibration mounts if worn.
      - Balance rotating parts.
      - Keep equipment clean.
    - Limit exposure:
      - Work out length of job.
      - Keep within action limits.
      - Don't grip too tightly.
      - Use job rotation.
      - Adequate rest breaks.
    - PPE:
      - Gloves to protect against cold and wet.

4. (a) Types of non-ionising radiation and their sources include:

- Ultraviolet light from welding, or excessive exposure to sunlight.
- Infrared radiation from laser equipment such as surveying measuring devices.
- Microwave radiation from communications dishes.
- Radio frequencies from communications transmitters.
- Electromagnetic radiation from high voltage electrical equipment.

You only needed to relate **TWO** of these to a construction source for part (a)

(b) The answer would ideally point out that the effects will depend on the type of non-ionising radiation a worker is exposed to.

Possible health effects could include:

- Photokeratitis (arc-eye) from welding.
- Retinal burns, corneal damage and cataracts from exposure to infra-red radiation.
- Burning of the skin from ultra-violet light or infra-red radiation (including sunlight).
- Heating of, and damage to, the skin and internal organs from radio frequencies and microwave radiation, and possible skin cancer.

Long Question

5. Noise reduction is very much a current issue, particularly since the introduction of the **Control of Noise at Work Regulations 2005**.

   (a) The decibel (dB) is a logarithmic unit measuring the magnitude of sound. In the unit "dB(A)", the (A) weighting corresponds to a frequency response which most closely resembles the characteristics of human hearing.

   (b) A number of options is available. They include:

   Change of process (e.g. use of solvents to carry out cleaning); reduction of air pressure; the use of silencers; re-positioning of compressors; noise transmission control measures such as erection of sound insulation barriers, absorbent materials positioned on walls and ceilings to reduce noise reflection; use of anti-vibration matting between the compressor and the floor to prevent transmission of noise through building structures. Mention of PPE should include mention of attenuation levels and the choice between plugs and ear defenders.

   (c) Selection criteria should include:

   Compatibility, comfort, CE marking, adequacy for the noise levels and frequency encountered and choice between ear plugs and defenders.

   Limitations depend on:

   Hygiene, comfort, incompatibility with other PPE and communication difficulties which could all result in users not wearing the equipment.

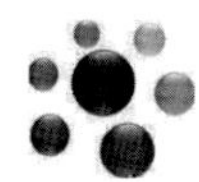

Element 10: Working at Height - Hazards and Risk Control

The main risks associated with work at height are:

- The worker falling from height.
- An object falling from height onto someone below.

Work Activities Involving a Risk of Injury

Typical work activities at height include:

- Roof construction/demolition and maintenance.
- Erecting and dismantling scaffolding.
- Window construction and cleaning.
- Any inspection or maintenance work (welding, pipework) which may also be done at ground level.

Basic Hazards and Risk Factors

- **Design** - of existing structures or materials to be worked on and the design of the task itself.
- **Distance of fall** - has a direct bearing on the severity of injury or damage. Possible distance should be minimised.
- **Roofs** (fragile, sloping and flat) - people are liable to fall through fragile roofs, roof lights, voids, holes or fragile material. Suitable barriers should be in place to prevent this happening.
- **Voids** - beneath roofs, should be treated as confined spaces. Often dusty with restricted access over fragile materials.
- **Deterioration of materials** - unsound materials may collapse under a person's weight causing fall; may break off and hit people or structures below.
- **Unprotected edges** - on access platforms/scaffolds; increases risk of falls or falling objects.
- **Unstable access equipment** - scaffolding may collapse or overturn under certain conditions due to incorrect erection; ladders may be unsecured, poorly maintained, misused or at the wrong angle; problems may arise when workers move from the access equipment onto the structure itself.
- **Weather and airflow** - may cause materials and people to be blown off a roof or scaffold; moisture can cause slippery surfaces; cold conditions may cause loss of dexterity.

- **Falling materials** - loose building materials and waste materials may fall from a height because they have been poorly stored or stacked or because constructions are crumbling. No material or object should be thrown from height where there is a risk of personal injury.

Methods of Avoiding Working at Height

Risk assessment should consider how activity at height could be avoided: modify a **process** or modify a **design**.

In most instances avoidance will not be possible and control measures for working at height are needed. Employers must adopt the following hierarchy:

- **Avoid** the need for work at height, e.g. eliminate the task or change the way in which the work is done.
- **Prevent** falls (of people and objects), e.g. provide appropriate work equipment or other appropriate measures. Collective measures are preferred to individual.
- **Minimise** the distance and consequences of falls, e.g. provide fall-arrest equipment or safety nets, etc.

Main Precautions to Prevent Falls and Falling Material

Good Design

Important design factors include:

- Safety features of access equipment.
- How equipment is erected and positioned.
- Task design, including methods used to lift and lower equipment and materials to and from work at height locations.
- Security of the access equipment, particularly in inclement weather.

Planning and Supervision of Work

Work at height needs to be planned in advance, with consideration of selection and use of work equipment. A safe system of work should take account of:

- Any supervision of workers that may be necessary, e.g. work equipment selected lower down the hierarchy, such as fall arrest equipment, requires a higher level of supervision.
- Any exposure to adverse weather conditions, e.g. maintenance on an icy roof or rainy conditions on a slippery surface.
- Any emergency or rescue arrangements required, e.g. falls while using a fall arrest system. It is not acceptable just to rely on the emergency services; this needs to be covered in the risk assessment and planned beforehand.

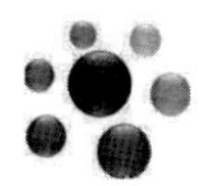

Avoidance of Work in Adverse Weather

If adverse weather is likely to jeopardise the safety of working at height, then work should be postponed until conditions are satisfactory. Getting weather forecasts daily is a suitable preliminary precaution. (This does not apply for emergency services.)

Emergency Rescue Plans

Consider emergency procedures for reasonably foreseeable circumstances.

- Methods need to be proportionate to risk.
- There should be no reliance on emergency services.
- Simple systems may suffice, but more detailed systems may be required depending on circumstances.

Arrangements should always be in place capable for rescuing a person. Those involved must be suitably trained and the required equipment must be available.

Requirements for Head Protection

Hard hats are PPE and offer protection against small falling objects, e.g. rubble or hand tools. They are not designed to protect against large heavy items falling on someone's head. Hard hats are not a replacement for other controls designed to prevent falling objects.

Hard hats should be worn whenever there is a foreseeable risk of injury to the head.

Inspection Requirements for Work Equipment

The **Work at Height Regulations 2005** require:

- Visual or more rigorous inspection by a competent person for safety purposes.
- Testing where appropriate.

An inspection must be made after the equipment has been assembled and as often as is necessary to ensure safety.

Any platform used in construction higher than 2m must be inspected in its place of use before being used. The inspection is only valid for seven days.

Inspection reports should be retained.

Safe Working Practices for Access Equipment and Roofwork

Scaffolding

Scaffolding is made up of the following basic components:

- **Standards** or **uprights** - vertical tubes used as a support for transferring a load to the ground or to a base plate.
- **Ledgers** - horizontal tubes tying the scaffold structure lengthways; they may also act as **guardrails**.
- **Transoms** - tubes spanning across ledgers to tie a scaffold across at right angles to the face of the building. They may also be used to support a **working platform**.

Tip: You should be able to sketch and label the features of a scaffold.

- **Independent Tied Scaffolds**

  Designed to carry its own weight and the full load of all materials and workers on the platform. It must be tied to the building where it is sited, to give stability and prevent movement. The total weight of the structure is supported by the ground

  Scaffold can be tied to the building using anchor bolts; through ties; rakers; and bracing (facade or ledger).

  Collapse of an independent tied scaffold may be caused by:

  - Overloaded work platform.
  - Scaffold built on soft ground without sole boards.
  - Scaffold not adequately tied to building.
  - Insufficient bracing incorporated into scaffold.
  - Standards not upright.
  - Standards bent, buckled or heavily corroded.
  - High winds.
  - Incorrect couplers used to join tubes together.
  - Scaffold struck by mobile plant.
  - Scaffold erected by incompetent workers.
  - Scaffold not properly inspected.

- **Putlog Scaffold**

  A putlog is a tube spanning from the ledger to the wall of a building. It is fixed into the brickwork by a spade end.

- **Fan Protection**

  Fans or protected walkways are often used to protect members of the public from falling materials and debris in busy city centres. They can also be used on construction or refurbishment projects.

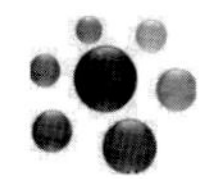

- **Cantilevered Scaffold**

  A form of independent scaffold that is entirely supported by the building. The scaffold has a framework inside the building which is wedged between the floors and the ceilings.

- **Mobile Tower Scaffolds**

  Light-duty scaffolds, commonly used for painting and simple maintenance jobs on buildings.

Safety Features of Scaffolding

- **Sole Boards** (or Sole Plates) - strong timber planks wider than a base plate. Long enough to be positioned under two base plates, providing extra load distribution capacity for the scaffold base.
- **Base Plates** - flat, square steel plates with a locating pin that must be inserted into the bottom of a standard to provide a bearing surface for load distribution.
- **Toeboards** - usually scaffold planks laid on their edge on the working platform to prevent small objects, e.g. rubble and tools, from being kicked off the platform.
- **Guardrails** - designed to prevent people from falling. Main guardrail should be at least 950mm above the working platform. Boarding may be used instead of an intermediate guardrail.
- **Debris Netting** - safety nets can also be used to prevent waste material or debris from falling by using them in the shape of a fan to protect those below.
- **Waste Chutes** - often used to dispose of debris and waste materials from scaffolding and roof work. Should be capped when not in use to prevent children using them as slides.

Requirements for Scaffold Erectors

Scaffold erection requires capability and fitness, skill, experience, knowledge and competence in order to complete scaffolding operations safely. Employers have a duty to ensure that anyone engaged in any such activity should be competent.

Scaffold erectors need to be trained in the following:

- Safe systems of work.
- Risks associated with scaffolding.
- Assessing site conditions.
- Use of PPE.
- Erecting, adapting and dismantling different types of scaffolding.
- Setting up hoists/lifting appliances.
- Operating mobile access platforms.

- Rigging and inspection of safety nets.
- Application of the **CDM Regulations 2015** and the **Work at Height Regulations 2005** in the operations above.

Means of Access

Scaffolding access is usually by way of ladders but may also involve the use of hoists and mobile elevating platforms.

Design of Loading Platforms

Loading platforms and any supporting structure must be set up and maintained by a competent person and should not be overloaded to avoid collapse, or buckling.

Scaffold Hoists

Various lifting appliances can be used to hoist both people and materials to a place of work, e.g. block and tackle hoists, wire ropes, chains, or slings.

Ensuring Stability

All structures must be rigid, stable and of sufficient strength to support working platforms and any load that might be placed on them, e.g. bricks, tools, equipment. Care is required to avoid impact from vehicles and possible collapse of the structure. There should be proper segregation, marking and lighting of structures.

- **Effects of Materials**

  An independent tied scaffold is designed to carry its own mass and full load of materials and workers used on it. The scaffold must also be tied to the building where it is sited, to give stability that prevents possible movement away from or towards the building. Tie methods include through or reveal ties, and eyebolts.

  The ground structure must be suitable to cope with the load. Base plates and sole plates are a vital safety consideration. Overloading with an excess of materials is liable to render the structure unstable.

- **Weather**

  Fluctuations in wind strength, rain, ice or snow must be taken into account. Footholds at heights are not as good as at ground level and balance is a more obvious problem. The carrying of large items, e.g. a roofing sheet, exaggerates the problem by acting as a 'sail'.

  When deciding whether to suspend work it is important to consider the wind speed, measures already taken to prevent falls, the height of the roof or work equipment and size of materials being handled.

- **Sheeting**
  - Debris netting is in an open meshwork reducing the risk of falling debris outside the work area.

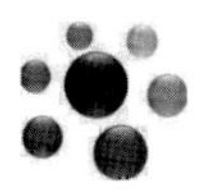

  - Scaffold sheeting is made of tough reinforced polythene material, often with eyelets to connect sheets together. It has a high tensile strength with tear and puncture resistance but dramatically increases wind loading.

- **Protection from Impact of Vehicles**

  Scaffolding on separated sites should be segregated and fenced off or coned off to prevent construction site vehicles impacting scaffolding members.

Inspection Requirements for Scaffolds

The **Work at Height Regulations 2005** require that all working platforms, including scaffolding, are inspected by a competent person:

- Before being used for the first time.
- After any substantial alteration.
- After an event likely to affect their strength or stability.
- Every 7 days.

Mobile Elevating Work Platforms (MEWPs)

MEWPs are motorised vehicles or trailers with powered extending arms supporting a work cradle.

Hazards of MEWPs	Safety Precautions for MEWPs
Falls from the working platform. Objects falling from the platform. Collapse of the MEWP. Overturn (toppling) of the MEWP. Instability on poor terrain/crossing uneven ground. Contact with live cables or overhead services. Unauthorised use.	Select type of MEWP to suit the terrain. Site on firm, stable ground. Ensure clearance from obstructions around and overhead when operating. Place barriers to prevent MEWP being struck by vehicles or mobile plant. Same barriers keep people from beneath the working platform (cradle). Cradle to have guardrails; safety harnesses to be worn as additional precaution. Controls of MEWP should be inside the cradle so operator at height has some control. MEWP not moved with cradle raised unless designed to do so. Must not be overloaded. Must be inspected (six-monthly) as item of lifting equipment designed to carry people. Restrict use to trained, authorised operators.

Use of Ladders, Step-Ladders, Trestles and Staging Platforms and Leading Edge Protection Systems

- **Ladders (including step-ladders and trestles)**

  Should only be used at height if risk assessment has shown that other more suitable work is not justified due to low-risk activity, or work is of short duration or because existing site features cannot be altered.

  Should be well-maintained and installed on sound and level bases. Ideal ladder angle is 75° to the horizontal or at a ratio of 1:4 distance away from the wall to height.

  Should be of the correct quality for the task and the environment (i.e. no metal ladders near unprotected live electrical circuits).

- **Step-Ladders and Trestles**

  The same safety precautions and general checks apply for both step-ladders and trestles.

  - **Trestles** - maintain free from defects, regularly inspect, do not paint, use on a firm, level base and fully open. Platforms based on trestles should be fully boarded, adequately supported and provided with edge protection (toeboards, guardrails). Where appropriate, access to platforms should be provided (step-ladder or ladder) and only one tier permitted when folding supports are used.
  - **Trestle scaffold** - not suitable for high-level work, generally used for light work, e.g. painting, decorating. Provides a working platform which can be supported by "A" frames, tripods, telescopic frames or split heads. Risk assess before use.

- **Staging Platforms**

  Are adaptable for use with guardrails. Available up to 6 metres in length for variable loads and situations.

- **Leading Edge Protection**

  Includes safety nets, birdcage scaffolding, safety harnesses, trolley systems, etc. (see later).

Other Access to Work at Height Techniques

- **Boatswain's Chair**

  Consists of a seat with a back and one or more suspension points. Used for light, short-term work.

- **Cradles**

  Suspended working platforms often seen suspended from the roofs of high-rise buildings - used for window cleaning work.

- **Rope Access**

  When not possible to work via a working platform, rope access may be used. Area beneath any of this type of work must be protected by fans, covered walkways or tunnels.

Fall Arrest Equipment

- **Harnesses**

  Useful when open edges have to be approached, e.g. during scaffold or steel erection. Operators must be fully trained.

- **Safety Nets**

  A means of arresting falls from height. Can be used on a variety of structures (e.g. towers, piers, bridges, chimneys, over motorways). A preferred method for industrial roof installation.

- **Air Bags/Soft Landing Systems**

  Used as a fall protection measure on construction projects.

- **Crash Decks**

  They are commonly semi-permanent structures (often inside a building) erected over machinery to protect it in the event of materials falling, e.g. in the event of a roof collapse. In public areas, use pedestrian tunnels or properly constructed false ceilings or crash decks to protect pedestrians from falling materials.

- **Emergency and Rescue Procedures**

  In selecting work equipment, employer must take account of need for easy and timely evacuation and rescue in the event of an emergency.

  This step is often neglected when work at height is being planned.

  Because rescue operations are often carried out under extreme pressure, consideration should be given to all aspects of the rescue process.

Roofwork

Certain precautions need to be taken during roofwork to ensure the protection of workers, occupants of buildings and members of the public.

Means of Access

Roof access must be carefully planned, including means for transporting tools/materials and removing waste. A number of methods may be used:

- Independent scaffolding provides safe access and to edges as well as any materials storage area.
- Fixed scaffold towers enable safe access, provided they are erected by a competent person and used in the proper manner.

- Mobile scaffold towers avoid the risks associated with scaffold erection. Equipment chosen must be carefully selected for the type of ground conditions present.
- For ladders, certain factors need to be taken into consideration, e.g. the length of ladder, which may be heavy and awkward to manoeuvre; the need to carry materials or tools, remembering that two hands should be free when climbing a ladder.
- If roof access is by a valley or parapet gutter and the adjacent roof is of fragile material, suitable covers are required to prevent a fall through the fragile material.

Edge Protection

Edge protection on roofs (flat or sloping) must be both high and strong enough to withstand a person rolling or sliding down or falling off. Protection may be permanent or temporary, e.g. guardrails or toeboards, depending on the roof structure.

Leading Edge Protection Systems

Working at the leading (working) edge gives rise to risks which can be controlled in a number of ways.

- **Safety Nets**

  Install by a competent person as close as possible to the roof surface and must be securely attached, of sufficient strength to withstand a person falling, and suited to the work.

- **Birdcage Scaffolding**

  Used for working inside factories, cinemas, churches, etc. to gain access to ceilings and walls for plastering, painting and decorating.

- **Safety Harnesses**

  Use running lines attached to a suitable anchorage point, mobile or fixed, e.g. a working platform. Should be fit for purpose and used in accordance with the manufacturer's instructions. The wearer should be trained in its use.

- **Trolley Systems**

  They are temporary barriers and may be installed at the leading edge. They require a safe system of work during installation, moving and dismantling, and must be able to be locked in position to prevent overturning.

- **Other Systems**

  Other leading edge systems:

  - Soft matting (where safety nets are not suitable), or
  - Air-filled bag systems.

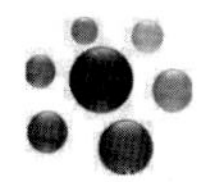

Crawling Boards

Crawling boards (together with roof ladders and edge protection) are required on most sloping roofs. They need to be fit for purpose, of sufficient strength to support workers, at least three rafters long, and able to be secured or placed so that they prevent any accidental movement.

Fall Arrest Equipment

Minimises the effect of a fall once it has happened and is used as part of a safe system of work.

Protection of Others

Other workers, occupants of buildings and members of the public should be protected from falling objects and persons by implementing the use of:

- **Demarcation**

  Suitable barriers at a safe distance from the roof edge are used to demarcate between access routes and working areas. Normally, two metres from the edge is an accepted distance to prevent falls.

- **Barriers, Tunnels, Signs, Marking and Lighting**

  The area below the roof work should be clearly segregated from vehicles and members of the public, particularly children and anyone with hearing or sight impairments by having safety nets, fan or birdcage scaffold. Dark or shadowy areas below roof work and scaffold should have barriers or tunnels with suitable signs, marking and lighting.

- **Sheeting, Netting and Fans**

  Sheeting combined with a second layer of scaffold boards or even plywood sheets can help to protect the public from falling objects and materials.

  Safety nets are of two main types: **personnel** nets or **material or protection** nets of a smaller mesh.

  Scaffold fans should be erected if there is any risk to pedestrians below or of passing vehicles being hit.

- **Head Protection**

  The provision and wearing of **head protection** during construction work is required by the **Personal Protective Equipment at Work Regulations 1992** and may prevent or reduce head injury due to falling or swinging objects and materials.

Working Over or Near Water

Working over or near water can present a risk of people slipping, tripping, falling or being knocked into water, being swept away or under water by strong currents and drowning. They can also be hit and injured by obstacles in the water.

When working over or near water, **regulations require** that:

- A risk assessment is required of the work involved, risk prevention and protective measures.
- All craft used to convey persons on water must be safe and be suitably constructed, maintained and operated by a competent person.
- Suitable rescue equipment must be provided nearby and persons trained/instructed in its use.
- Guardrails must be in place if a person can fall from the edge of adjacent land, a structure, scaffolding or a floating stage (removed only for the movement of materials).
- Where full scaffolding or gangways (with handrails/toeboards) are not practicable, safety nets can be used.
- Where safety nets are not practicable, safety harnesses can be worn, but need secure anchor points and must be worn and attached at all times.
- Employers must do everything that is reasonably practicable to provide information, instruction, training and supervision.
- Employers must provide a safe place and system of work with safe access/egress and must ensure that provision is made for safe use and handling of materials, etc.

Additional Appropriate Control Measures

A number of precautions can contribute to the safety of individuals and groups of people by preventing them from falling into water, or providing aid if they do fall in.

- **Warning Notices**

  Erected at all edges and boundaries near water so they can be easily seen by anyone approaching.

- **Scaffolds and Temporary Working Platforms**

  Erected by qualified competent persons and inspected according to the regulations. Best method of ensuring safe working over water. Designed and inspected for the task; stable; and of sufficient size for the proposed work.

- **Buoyancy Aids**

  Life-jackets or buoyancy aids must be worn where there is a risk of drowning when working on or near water, and at all times while working on boats.

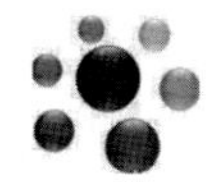

- **Life-jacket** - will provide sufficient buoyancy to turn and support even an unconscious person face upwards.
- **Buoyancy aid** - worn to provide extra buoyancy to assist a conscious person in keeping afloat.

Either type will depend on an assessment of: water conditions; work being undertaken; protective clothing being worn; proximity of assistance; and competency as a swimmer.

- **Safety Boat**

  Safe transport of any person conveyed by water to or from his/her place of work is a requirement of **CDM 2015**. Passenger-carrying craft must:

  - Not be overcrowded or overloaded.
  - Be marked with maximum number of persons and limits of operation.
  - Be suitably constructed and maintained.
  - Be inspected if they carry more than 12 passengers at any one time, and a worthiness certificate obtained.
  - Carry appropriate life-saving and fire-fighting appliances/equipment.
  - Be under the control of a competent person.

  Communication required during any work activity on or in the vicinity of water, and in the event of an emergency.

- **Platforms and Gangways**

  Platforms or gangways must comply with the requirements of **CDM 2015**. Working platforms must be properly constructed, sufficiently stable, and have good anchorage and ballasting.

- **Ladders**

  Any ladders used for access must meet all usual requirements and be of sufficient length; extend at least five rungs above a stepping-off point; and be securely lashed to prevent slipping.

- **Housekeeping**

  All tools, equipment and rubbish should be stored away, stacked safely or disposed of. Contaminants should be cleaned off or treated to prevent slips/injuries and minimise fire hazards.

- **Illumination**

  Essential for night work, and in shafts, dark corners and stairways. Illumination should always include the immediate water surface and spotlights may be used to help locate a person in the water. Requirements should be checked with the appropriate authorities.

- **Weather Conditions**

  The local weather forecast should be obtained and employees informed prior to each day's work or shift.

- **First-Aid Equipment**

  First-aid facilities and first-aiders or an appointed person are required. The facilities/equipment available should be readily accessible and include portable equipment for resuscitation and transportation of any casualties.

- **Protective Clothing and Equipment**

  Safety helmets must be worn at all times. Anyone struck on the head before falling into water is at a particular risk of drowning.

  Footwear with non-slip soles should be worn. Rubber and/or thigh boots should be avoided.

  Safety harnesses and safety belts are permitted where it is not possible to provide a standard working platform or safety net, provided that they are always worn and always secured to a safe anchorage. Operatives must be trained and instructed in use.

- **Lifebuoys/Rescue Lines**

  Lifebuoys and rescue lines should be provided at appropriate locations. Potential users require regular training and instruction. Regular checks should ensure they remain in their proper place, are intact, and not in need of repair.

- **Safe Operating Procedure**

  When work over or near water is carried out, it is vital that:

  - Continual checks are made to ensure that no one is missing.
  - No lone working occurs.
  - Operatives work in pairs so that someone can raise the alarm.
  - Appropriate training is given to all personnel in emergency procedures.

- **Rescue Procedure**

  Rescue procedures should be practised regularly. Personnel should be trained and instructed in safe rescue procedures, especially if a casualty is injured, too heavy, fully clothed, or in a state of panic.

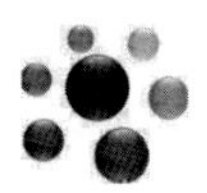

Exam-Style Questions

Short Questions

1. (a) **Give FOUR** reasons why an item may fall from height on a construction site. (4 marks)

   (b) **Describe FOUR** workplace precautions that might be used to prevent items falling from height. (4 marks)

   (Total: 8 marks)

2. (a) **Outline** the main hazards associated with the use of ladders at work. (3 marks)

   (b) **Describe** how these hazards may be eliminated or reduced. (5 marks)

   (Total: 8 marks)

3. **Outline** the safety measures that can be taken to prevent falls from height associated with stairwells and other holes/openings in floors that are created during the construction of a multi-storey building. (8 marks)

4. **Identify** the components and features to be examined when carrying out the routine inspection of a typical putlog scaffold. (8 marks)

Long Question

5. Refurbishment and repair work is to be undertaken on the flat roof of a two-storey, high-security office block. The work will include replacement of the waterproof membrane. The only access route for the roofing workers is from inside the building. The only external access route for materials is via an electrically driven, lightweight, inclined builders' hoist.

   Explain the procedures necessary for:

   (a) The safety of the office workers who will occupy the building during the project. (5 marks)

   (b) The safety of the construction workers who will be carrying out the work on the roof. (5 marks)

   (c) The safe installation, operation and dismantling of the inclined builders' hoist. (10 marks)

   (Total: 20 marks)

Model Answers

Short Questions

1. (a) On a construction site, an item may fall from a height due to:

    - Deterioration of the structure.
    - Inappropriate storage.
    - Poor housekeeping.
    - Gaps in the platform.
    - Lack of edge protection.
    - Incorrect methods for lifting or lowering.

    (Only four are required.)

    (b) Workplace precautions to prevent items falling from a height are:

    - Physical safeguards - barriers, close boarding, use of nets and toeboards.
    - Supervision.
    - Good housekeeping.
    - Procedures and safe systems of work.

2. (a) The main hazards associated with the use of ladders at work are:

    - Poor maintenance.
    - Incorrect use of the ladder.
    - Incorrect footing.

    (b) These hazards may be eliminated or reduced by:

    - Correct inspection.
    - Correct storage.
    - Correct securing.
    - The correct angle (1:4 or 75° to the horizontal).
    - Correct section use.
    - Training of operators.
    - Tied to structure.
    - Footed.
    - Long enough.

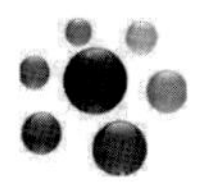

3. The safety measures taken to prevent falls associated with stairwells and other holes in floors:
    - Provision of guardrails for stairwells and lift shafts
    - Provision of hand rails on stairs
    - Fixing covers over other holes in floors
    - Providing adequate levels of lighting
    - Ensuring a good standard of housekeeping
    - Ensuring a high standard of supervision and control.

4. Components and features to be examined when inspecting a putlog scaffold:
    - The nature of the ground where the scaffold is sited
    - The provision of sole boards and base plates beneath standards that are plumb and evenly spread
    - Bedding of putlogs into the brickwork and correct orientation
    - Condition of the brickwork
    - Correct installation of bridles and clips
    - The provision of adequate ties and bracing
    - Working platform - fully boarded with toe boards and guard rails
    - Access ladder in good condition, suitable length and tied.

Long Question

5. (a) The procedures necessary to ensure the safety of the office workers:

   - Issues relating to fire alarms.
   - The provision of additional extinguishers.
   - Ensuring that existing evacuation procedures are not compromised.
   - A system of daily liaison with the occupiers to ensure integrity of local arrangements (protection of those entering/leaving the building).
   - Brief occupying staff on particular hazards and the work in general.
   - Protection from falling materials onto routes of access.
   - Segregation of construction workers from regular users.

   (b) The issues relating to the safety of construction workers working on the roof:

   - The provision of training and information.
   - Specific training for additional loads that could be taken onto the roof.
   - Protection from roof edge and from roof lights.
   - Precautions to be taken in the use of bitumen boilers.
   - Provision of fire extinguishers.
   - Procedures for evacuation in event of a fire.
   - Provision of safe means of access to and egress from the roof.

   (c) The procedures necessary to ensure safe installation, operation and dismantling of the inclined hoist:

   - Hoist to be erected and used by competent personnel only.
   - Arrangements for inspection, testing, regular maintenance.
   - Guarding of dangerous parts of machinery.
   - Integrity of any electrical installation.

   Protection is also required at the base and the top of the hoist and means provided to ensure security of the load as it travels to the roof.

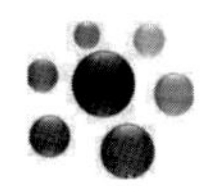

Element 11: Excavation Work and Confined Spaces - Hazards and Risk Control

Excavation Work - Hazards and Assessment

Excavations involve work below ground level and are defined in the **Construction (Design and Management) Regulations 2015** as including any earthwork, trench, well, shaft, tunnel or underground working.

- **Buried Services**

  Contact with buried services such as electricity cables and gas pipes, water mains, drains and sewers, which on fracturing can release dangerous substances or cause fire and explosion.

- **Falls of Persons/Equipment/Material into Excavations**

  This can be due to unprotected edges, the use of badly sited access ladders and badly constructed ramps used for vehicular access.

- **Collapse of Sides**

  Additional loads caused by machinery and vehicles nearby may lead to the collapse of sides, if these are not battered (sloped back) or shored up. Loose or unstable earth around an excavation or at the bottom may collapse.

- **Collapse of Adjacent Structures**

  Digging too close to foundations which support nearby buildings may undermine the support and precipitate its collapse. This would be compounded in the event of a collapse of the excavation itself.

- **Water Ingress**

  Water ingress or flooding may occur due to weather conditions or from underground watercourses. When working below water level, e.g. near to rivers, canals, docks artificial structures such as cofferdams or caissons may be needed to dam back the water.

- **Use of Cofferdams and Caissons**

  Structures which are pumped dry to allow work to be carried out inside them below the waterline.

  They must be suitably designed and constructed to prevent the ingress of water (or other materials), or appropriately equipped to pump out water and provide shelter and escape should water or materials enter.

- **Contaminated Ground**

  There may be contaminated ground at the site of excavation due to residues contained in it from previous industrial use/activities or stored or dumped on the land.

- **Toxic and Asphyxiating Atmospheres**

  Digging may uncover **buried materials or contaminants within the ground** hazardous to health (i.e. flammable or toxic gases; chemical and metal compounds). These may be the result of the decomposition of organic matter or from the dumping/spillage of hazardous substances.

- **Mechanical Hazards**

  Mechanical hazards can be due to vehicles (e.g. mobile cranes, mobile plant) falling into the excavations or passing too close to an excavation, causing the sides to collapse. Excavators represent a significant hazard in respect of both the risk of collision with the moving digging arm and scoop, and materials falling from the scoop when being lifted and manoeuvred.

Overhead Hazards Including Power Lines

Work beneath overhead services and power lines should be avoided.

All overhead services should be identified and any diversions or disconnections ensured before excavation work begins.

Three situations arise in construction work at overhead power lines:

- No scheduled excavation work or passage of plant to take place under the lines.
- Excavation plant and equipment will pass beneath the power lines.
- Excavation work will take place beneath the power lines.

Risk Assessment

Risk assessments under **MHSWR 1999** and **CDM Regulations 2015** should consider:

- Depth of excavation.
- Soil type - non-cohesive ground or light soil; cohesive ground or heavy soil; rock.
- Type of work involved, e.g. at the side of a road; in a housing development; laying pipes/cables; trenches; pits.
- Type and use of mechanical equipment.
- Proximity of the excavation to roadways, structures, schools, hospitals.
- Presence of the public/children.
- Weather - summer, winter.

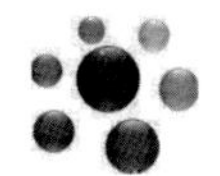

Control Measures for Excavation Work

Controls

The **CDM Regulations 2015** call for effective management of excavation work under the supervision of a competent person to ensure:

- **Identification, detection and marking of buried services** and all cables by checking with local service providers and reviewing surveys and plans.

  Safe digging methods particularly when exposing cables and pipes and using spades and shovels instead of excavators. Damage to cables should be reported immediately to the appropriate services.

- **Methods of Supporting Excavations**

  Use of excavation supports to prevent the collapse of the side walls of an excavated area. The **CDM Regulations** require that support work (including dismantling) may only be done by, or under the direction of, a competent person. Methods of supporting excavation are:

  - **Battering** which relies on the properties of the earth to form a stable sloping pile (i.e. angle of repose).
  - **Shoring** which uses artificial support for the side walls of an excavation where the angle of repose in the excavation is greater than the natural angle for the type of material.

- **Means of Access**

  Ladders provide the main means of access to and egress from an excavation. They must be suitably secured to prevent undue movement and extend above the excavation to give the necessary height required for a safe handhold (at least 1.05 metres).

- **Crossing Points**

  Crossing points in an excavation should be at designated points and be of sound construction to support all types of vehicles and equipment. Gangways across excavations should have guardrails and toeboards.

- **Barriers**

  Barriers are required to protect the edge of an excavation to prevent falls of people, materials and vehicles. Fencing and boarding may also be required to protect both employees and members of the public.

- **Lighting and Warning Signs**

  Lighting and warning signs warn of the presence of an excavation and of any special measures to be taken on entering a site. Signs should be clearly visible and there should be a good level of lighting.

- **Safe Storage of Spoil**

  Safe storage of spoil will depend on the space available to stack it - the minimum distance of a spoil heap from an excavation is 0.6m.

- **De-Watering and Use of Freezing Equipment**

  De-watering involves the disposal of any water arising from surface water run-off and ground water and should be discussed with the appropriate environmental agency.

- **Positioning and Routeing of Vehicles, Plant and Equipment**

  Positioning and routeing of vehicles, plant and equipment should be carefully considered to prevent objects falling into excavations.

- **Personal Protective Equipment**

  The need for PPE is determined by the nature of the work being carried out (i.e. breathing equipment in tunnels and shafts; face shields for welding work; hearing protection where there is excessive noise) but hard hats are required at all times.

Particular Requirements for Contaminated Ground

Soil testing to show the presence of any contaminants must be carried out by competent persons from an accredited laboratory and the workforce must be screened by medical practitioners to ensure no serious health conditions arise.

Inspection Requirements for Excavation Support

Construction work in an excavation requiring supports or battering cannot start until it has been inspected by a competent person - the **CDM Regulations** require that inspections take place before each shift. Additional inspections will be required after any event likely to have affected the strength or stability of the excavation such as flooding or collapse. A report must be made and records kept of such inspections.

When work in the excavation is completed, support materials should be safely removed by experienced workers and a competent person should inspect the site to ensure that all dangerous materials and equipment have been removed. Filling should use only appropriate materials and be conducted in a controlled manner under the direction of a competent person. Uncontrolled tipping is an offence.

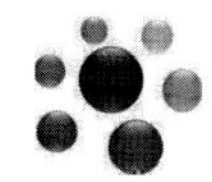

Confined Space Working - Hazards and Risks

Meaning of 'Confined Space'

A confined space is an enclosed space where there is a reasonably foreseeable specified risk of any serious injury associated with it (i.e. typically, trenches, sewers, manholes, tunnels, excavations, chambers, tanks, pits, cellars and unventilated rooms).

Typical Confined Spaces in Construction

The **Confined Spaces Regulations 1997** outline the legal requirements:

- Avoid entry to confined spaces, e.g. by doing the work from outside.
- Follow a safe system of work if entry to a confined space is unavoidable, and put in place adequate emergency arrangements before the work starts.

Due to the nature of the work itself, i.e. where there are risks from machinery, electricity or hazardous substances, other legislation may be involved.

Hazards and Risks Associated with Confined Spaces

- Exposure to **toxic atmospheres** (i.e. poisonous gas and fumes from petrols and solvents); **explosive or flammable atmospheres** (i.e. acetylene, propane, butane) and **oxygen deficient/enriched atmospheres** (i.e. due to oxidation/combustion/carbon dioxide).
- **Hot conditions** can raise body temperature to a dangerous level and cause unconsciousness, fatigue or stress.
- **Water** can cause disease (i.e. hepatitis, Weil's disease) and drowning.
- **Free-flowing solids** (i.e. cement, sand) can make the environment irrespirable.
- **Restricted space** calls for physically fit and agile workers, able to work in confined areas and wear breathing apparatus if necessary. The enclosed area may make it difficult to work with machinery and call for special precautions to avoid electric shock or asphyxiation due to gas or fumes.

Control Measures for Confined Space Working

Precautions for Safe Entry

A risk assessment must be carried out to establish control measures and a safe system of work that will take into account:

- **Avoidance Where Possible**

  No person shall enter a confined space to carry out work unless it is not reasonably practicable to achieve that purpose without such entry. Better work-planning or a different approach can reduce the need for confined space working, e.g. modify the confined space itself so that entry is not necessary; have the work done from outside, e.g. blockages can be cleared in underground chambers by use of remotely operated rotating flail devices, vibrators or air purgers; inspection, sampling and cleaning operations can often be done from outside the space using appropriate equipment and tools; remote cameras can be used for internal inspection of vessels.

So far as is reasonably practicable, no person shall enter or carry out work in (other than in an emergency) or leave a confined space otherwise than in accordance with a system of work which, in relation to the specified risks, renders that work safe and without risks to health.

- **Risk Assessment**

  A risk assessment appropriate for work in confined spaces (**Confined Spaces Regulations 1997**) will identify the risks present and determine what precautions to take, in relation to:

  - The task.
  - The working environment.
  - Working materials and tools.
  - The suitability of those carrying out the task.
  - Arrangements for emergency rescue.

  Preliminary planning of confined space entry is important to establish whether entry can be avoided or if required, whether breathing equipment will be needed. A permit-to-work will:

  - Identify who may authorise particular jobs (and any limits to their authority) and who is responsible for specifying the necessary precautions (e.g. isolation, gas testing, emergency arrangements, etc.).
  - Ensure that contractors engaged to carry out work are included.
  - Provide training and instruction in the issue of permits.
  - Monitor and audit to ensure that the system works as intended.

  Assessment will identify whether access to the confined space can be avoided, or the nature of the work required and the steps needed to make the job safe.

- **Permit-to-Work**

  Requirements of a permit laid out in the safe system of work include:

  - Hazard **identification**.
  - Hazard **control**.
  - **Isolation** of mechanical and electrical equipment.
  - **Permit system** in writing (a separate 'hot work permit' is required for operations which could provide a source of ignition, such as riveting, welding, cutting, burning or heating).
  - **Employee information and training** - signs that warn of hazards and barriers that prohibit unauthorised entry; additional training on use of fire-fighting equipment.

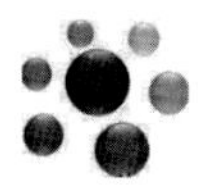

- **Equipment** - testing and monitoring PPE and rescue equipment.
- **Rescue** procedures and equipment necessary to rescue entrants from confined spaces must be in place, e.g. rescue harnesses, lifting tripod, resuscitator, first-aid kit, communication equipment, stretchers.
- Protection from **external hazards** particularly in traffic areas.
- **Duty to other employers and contractors** by using sentries and maintaining continuous contact with entrants.
- Training and use of competent persons.

Training should cover the permit-to-work, respiratory equipment, gas-testing equipment, rescue procedures, first-aid treatment including artificial respiration, evacuation and emergency procedures, fire-fighting, and communication procedures. Competent persons are required for gas testing who are competent not only to use the instrumentation but also interpret the results.

- **Training**

  No person should be allowed to enter a confined space unless they are trained and competent to do so. Training should be refreshed regularly and records should be kept of all types of training carried out.

- **Atmospheric Testing**

  Atmospheric testing at all locations should be carried out by a competent person using a suitable gas detector which is correctly calibrated to determine any condition dangerous to life or health or any likelihood of explosion.

- **Means of Access**

  A safe method of access/egress should be provided to allow ready access to and egress from the confined space itself. Only authorised persons may enter and only if wearing securely attached harness or rope. Breathing equipment is not necessary if materials giving off dangerous fumes/vapours have been removed or if there is a supply of air for respiration.

- **Personal Protective Equipment**

  Following a risk assessment, appropriate protective equipment needs to be worn and might include hard hats, coveralls, boots, Wellingtons, breathing apparatus sets, gloves and/or safety spectacles, radios.

Monitoring Arrangements

Monitoring must be carried out in accordance with the permit requirements by a competent person.

Emergency Arrangements

The **Confined Spaces Regulations 1997** require that no person shall work in a confined space unless suitable and sufficient arrangements for their rescue in an emergency have been made. The rescue plan must be communicated to all personnel involved before commencing work.

Exam-Style Questions

Short Questions

1 (a) **Identify FOUR** of the specific risks that are associated with the definition of a confined space. (4 marks)

(b) **Give FOUR** specific examples of confined spaces that may be encountered on construction sites. (4 marks)

(Total: 8 marks)

2. **Outline** the typical control measures that should be in place before and during excavation work in order to help reduce risks associated with the work. (8 marks)

3. The mains water supply to a large building complex is to be repaired.

   Outline the safety precautions needed for the excavation work so that the risk of injury to the workers doing the work and others is minimised. (8 marks)

4. Repair work to an underground reservoir will require the use of compressed air-powered tools to remove defective concrete. It will also require the use of epoxy resin material to make the repairs. **Describe** the health risks to the workers engaged in this work. (8 marks)

Long Question

5. Maintenance work on a construction site means it is necessary to enter a large cement silo.

   (a) **Identify** the foreseeable hazards associated with the cement silo entry. (5 marks)

   (b) **Outline** the safety precautions to be taken before and during the work to reduce the risks to workers entering the silo. (15 marks)

(Total: 20 marks)

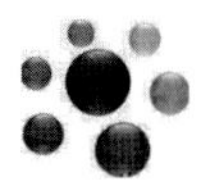

Model Answers

Short Questions

1. (a) Possible confined space risks are:

    Presence of toxic, flammable or explosive fumes or vapours; lack of oxygen; oxygen enrichment; ingress of fluids; falls of materials; restriction of space causing injury to the head (bumps); claustrophobic effects.

    (b) Examples of confined spaces on a construction site:

    Manholes; sewers; tunnels; excavations; tanks; chambers; pits; unventilated rooms.

2. Control measures needed to improve safety before and during excavation work include:

    - Initial plan to decide a safe method of excavation, particularly if hand-digging close to services is required.
    - Assessing the land – is there contamination?
    - Providing adequate support for the sides (e.g. shoring or benching) where there is a risk of collapse.
    - Detecting underground services such as water, gas and electricity by using plans and cable or pipe detectors.
    - Storing materials, equipment and spoil away from the edges.
    - Providing measures such as stop blocks to prevent vehicles falling into the excavation.
    - Protecting pedestrians using edge protection such as guard rails or barriers.
    - Providing pumps to protect against flooding.
    - Supporting adjacent buildings and structures against collapse.
    - Providing safe access to and egress from the excavation.
    - Testing deep excavations for fumes and providing necessary ventilation.
    - Competent persons regularly inspecting the excavations.
    - Using PPE such as hard hats and safety footwear.
    - Having procedures to deal with biological hazards or contaminants.
    - Having emergency procedures in place, including rescue plans.

    (Only eight are required.)

3. The safety precautions needed during the excavations to protect workers:
   - Consideration of stability of adjacent buildings.
   - Detection of underground services and safe digging practices close to services.
   - Trench supports (collapse) and supporting exposed services.
   - Safe access/egress, edge protection.
   - Keeping materials/vehicles away from edge.
   - Precautions against flooding (isolation of water main).
   - Atmospheric testing.
   - PPE (falling objects).
   - Lighting.
   - Co-ordination between contractors and client (hospital management).
   - Supervision; trench inspections.
   - Emergency procedures.
   - Signage; barriers.
   - Possible obstruction of emergency exits from hospital (re-routeing).
4. The hazardous situations giving rise to health risks are as follows:
   - Excessive noise leading to noise induced hearing loss.
   - Hand-arm vibration syndrome arising from the use of hand tools.
   - Musculoskeletal disorders occurring due to working in cramped conditions or the weight of tools and equipment.
   - Breathing problems could occur due to working in the enclosed, dusty environment.
   - Respiratory sensitisation in the long-term due to inhalation of the fumes from epoxy resins.
   - Possible asphyxiation due to the presence of methane or an oxygen-depleted environment.

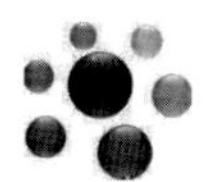

Long Question

5. (a) The foreseeable hazards associated with cement silo entry are:

   - Residues of the contents (cement).
   - Working at height.
   - Access and egress difficulties.
   - Oxygen deficiencies.
   - Poor levels of lighting.

   (b) Safety precautions to be taken on entering the silo:

   - The use of PPE (helmets, boots gloves, hearing protection).
   - The use of a permit-to-work system.
   - Atmospheric testing.
   - Provision of adequate lighting.
   - Isolation and lock-off of services.
   - The use of competent and experienced workers.

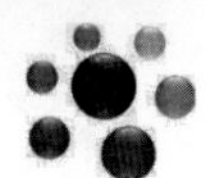

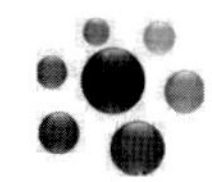

Element 12: Demolition and Deconstruction - Hazards and Risk Control

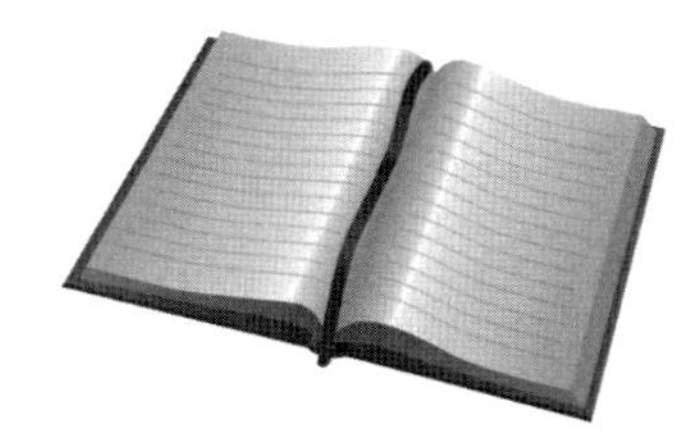

Demolition and Deconstruction Hazards and Risk

- **Demolition** is the deliberate pulling down, destruction or taking apart of a structure, or a substantial part of a structure (usually not for re-use).
- **Deconstruction** (also referred to as 'dismantling') is the taking down of all, or a substantial part, of a structure (often for re-use).
- **Piecemeal demolition** uses hand-held tools or machines to gradually reduce the building down to ground level.
- **Deliberate controlled collapse** - this is carried out using explosives or pre-weakening the structure followed by remote mechanical demolition or pulling using a wire rope.
- **Pre-weakening** is the removal of key structural members to cause complete collapse of the whole or part of the building or structure.
- **Progressive demolition** is the controlled removal of sections of the structure, retaining the stability of the remainder and avoiding collapse of the whole or part of the building.

The appropriate method should be selected based on the location of the site and information about the structure to be demolished.

Basic Hazards and Factors Relating to Demolition

- **Equipment to be Used**

  Hand tools - requires less set-up time. Care should be taken to ensure scaffolding meets certain specifications. Crawling boards should be used where roofwork is involved (consider use of harnesses and edge protection). Care should be taken when removing large structures (lifting hazards) and materials containing radioactive waste or asbestos.

Machines - machine demolition can be carried out in a number of ways. In all cases the operators are required to be well trained and supervised and the equipment subject to regular maintenance inspections. The equipment should adequately protect the operator, e.g. shatterproof windows, steel mesh/bars and operators must be protected by respirators when asbestos dust or other health hazards may be present. Certain structures, e.g. chimneys, pre-stressed concrete, brick or masonry viaducts, require more specific precautions and each case should be looked at individually to assess the problems it presents. Machine checks should be carried out regularly to ensure lights, braking systems, steering, hydraulics, tyres, wheels, etc. are in order.

- **Premature Collapse**

  Premature collapse of buildings and structures is the main cause of accidents in demolition work and often due to a failure to plan at an early stage. Dilapidation of the structure prior to work starting increases the risk.

- **Falls and Falling Materials**

  Falls from workplaces or access routes are commonplace. Lack of planning may lead to workers devising their own means of access and methods of work.

  Methods of work should make it unnecessary for working at heights.

  Falling materials can be due to intentional dropping of materials or an unexpected collapse. Falling materials can also be associated with falling loads or equipment and the lifting of loads over areas of public access.

- **Plant, Vehicles and Other Equipment Overturning**

  Transport-related accidents in demolition work are common due to poor control of vehicle movements and potential proximity of private or road-going trade vehicles to heavy demolition plant.

- **Manual Handling**

  Manual handling is one of five main priority areas identified by HSE for construction site safety. Approximately a third of all reportable construction industry accidents involve manual handling tasks.

  Damaging work postures are likely to involve stooping and kneeling and arms raised above shoulder height. There is a high incidence of MSDs affecting the lower back, knees, shoulder and neck areas due to poor working postures. Long-term disability is common.

- **Dust and Fume**

  The production of dust is a common hazard during demolition. It may be irritant, toxic, corrosive, cause eye injuries or carry fungal or bacterial matter.

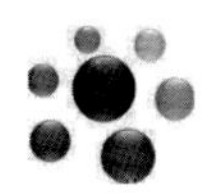

Dusts are divided into two categories dependent on size. Those causing ill-health effects are below 10µ in diameter. Respirable dusts are below 7µ in size and damage the alveoli causing chronic respiratory disease. Demolition dusts often contain silica compounds, waste cement, plaster products and possibly Asbestos-Containing Materials (ACMs).

Fumes are solid particles and form an oxide in contact with air. They are generated by processes which involve metal heating/melting.

- **Noise and Vibration**

  Demolition is inherently noisy. Noise or vibration levels may cause nuisance to surrounding communities.

- **Existence of Services**

  Before any demolition work can commence all underground and overhead services (e.g. electricity, gas, water, telecommunications) must be identified and located and the corresponding disconnections built into the demolition plan.

- **Hazardous Substances**

  Dangerous substances such as asbestos, polychlorinated biphenyls (PCBs), lead paint, flammable liquids, any unidentified materials, drums, packages, radioactive materials and residual material in pipelines or tanks can pose serious hazards to workers and may be found in buildings or surrounding ground.

  The method statement and demolition plan should outline how the presence of such hazardous substances is to be identified and the means of their disposal. Requirement for any PPE should also be identified.

- **Dilapidation** (lit: 'a state of disrepair or ruin')

  Dilapidation can add to the hazards of the demolition work, by leaving services exposed, or hidden by debris. Such debris also hides holes and voids, adding danger to the already long list of hazards. Dilapidation should be considered in the pre-demolition survey.

Demolition Appropriate Control Measures

- **Avoidance of Premature Collapse**

  Designers should consider structural stability and include relevant information with their designs in order to avoid premature collapse. Adequate temporary structural supports for shoring and propping up structures should be used in accordance with the appropriate standards and should be sufficient and suitable for the work required. Where scaffolding is required, it should normally be an independent tied scaffold.

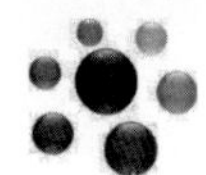

- **Protection from Falls and Falling Materials**

  Before and during demolition operations, site managers should ensure that all site personnel and contractors can get to their place of work safely and that exclusion zones prevent people from accessing demolition areas. Scaffolds, permanent access stairs or catwalks used by demolition personnel should be kept in a safe condition, for as long as possible.

  Fire exit routes should not be obstructed and possibly fire-retardant sheeting and netting used. Windows should be boarded up to prevent materials falling or being ejected. Lifting loads over areas of public access should be avoided where possible or alternative pedestrian routes put in place.

- **Siting and Use of Plant and Machinery**

  Plant and machinery should be properly sited within a compound and isolated at the end of each shift.

- **Dust and Fume**

  Protection against dust and fume from demolition activities may include a **COSHH** assessment, maintaining a high standard of housekeeping and using techniques that produce low levels of dust (damping down).

- **Noise and Vibration**

  The local authority Environmental Health Department should be informed when any particularly disruptive activities take place. A noise assessment (the **Control of Noise at Work Regulations 2005**) will identify potentially noise-sensitive areas on site and actions to reduce noise levels (i.e. using plant and equipment with low operating noise levels and mains-generated electricity in preference to diesel generators; placing solid-panelled fencing around the site instead of wire fences; restricting deliveries to daytime working hours, i.e. not early morning or late at night).

  Vibration levels must not exceed 10mm/sec at any nearby buildings.

- **Protection of the Environment**

  Environmental information relating to any underground tanks or potential chemical/biological hazards or the presence of contaminated land, along with the building's former use, should be supplied to the contractor prior to demolition.

  Contaminated sites may include gasworks; power stations; sewage treatment works; railway land; oil refineries and petrol stations; chemical works; asbestos works; slaughter yards and abattoirs; paper and printing works; hospitals.

  Waste management planning is important here, e.g. on-site segregation, "reduce, re-use, recycle" principles, carriage and disposal of waste.

  All the information should be included in the health and safety plan for the demolition project.

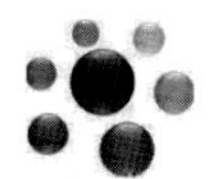

- **Competence of the Workforce**

  All personnel should be competent for the tasks that they undertake. The **CDM Regulations 2015** place responsibilities on the client and other persons involved with demolition works to ensure that competent persons are employed on the project (discussed elsewhere under the **CDM Regulations**).

Pre-Demolition Investigation and Survey

The survey should identify:

- The nature and method of construction of the building including any drawings, etc. In their absence a structural engineer report and a demolition survey for asbestos may be needed. The current state of repair of the structure should also be considered.
- Type of structures and location of services.
- Presence of dangerous substances or contaminated land.
- Previous use of the premises and site storage facilities for machinery, oils and fuels.
- Waste disposal; removal and storage of rubble from the immediate area during demolition and its eventual removal off-site.
- Safe access and egress onto and around the site for vehicles and pedestrian traffic and emergency vehicles must be maintained.

Purpose and Scope of Pre-Demolition, Deconstruction or Refurbishment Survey

Duties

The **property owner** (or person in control of the premises) has a duty to ensure that a pre-demolition survey is carried out on non-domestic premises for both notifiable and non-notifiable CDM projects. For refurbishment or deconstruction, the local authority building department should be consulted before any structural alterations are made.

An **MDHS 100 Type 3 asbestos survey** is often included in a full survey.

Carrying Out the Survey

Pre-demolition, deconstruction or refurbishment surveys are to be carried out by **competent persons**.

Its **purpose** is to carry out a thorough structural survey and assessment before any potentially load-bearing parts of a structure are altered. It will consider:

- **Key Structural Elements**

  Structural collapse is to be prevented, so all key structural elements of the building are to be identified. The competent person will decide on the suitable method of demolition and the design and nature of any temporary structural supports required. During the work, structures are never to be overloaded.

- **Services**

  The location and identification of any services are to be determined. Integral, underground or overhead services are likely to be encountered in demolition, refurbishment or deconstruction projects.

- **Dilapidation**

  The extent of any dilapidation is to be determined, identifying the locations and significance of its effects on the structures involved in the work.

- **Review**

  A review should be made of the existing health and safety file and any drawings and structural calculations that may be relevant. This will give an indication of the effects that the demolition, deconstruction or refurbishment may have on the structures and nearby structures.

- **Structural Alterations**

  All previous alterations to the structure should also be reviewed and compared with the health and safety file, calculations, drawings, etc., to ensure the significance of any change does not adversely affect the current project work.

Control Measures Included in a Method Statement

Demolition Method Statement

To comply with the **CDM Regulations 2015** a written method statement is necessary for all demolition work. This sets out the sequence of work and will include proposals relating to the pre-demolition survey and preferred method of working.

The method statement should:

- Be drawn up before work starts.
- Be communicated to all involved.
- Identify the work procedure, associated problems and their solutions.

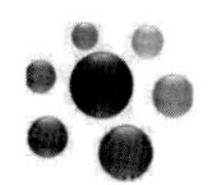

- Be easily understood and agreed by all workers at whatever level.
- Form a reference for site supervision.

The demolition method statement should include:

- Name/address of demolition contractor and site.
- Sequence/method of demolition.
- Details of personnel access, working platforms and machinery requirements.
- Details of any pre-weakening of structures to be pulled down or demolished using explosives, and temporary propping required.
- Arrangements for the protection of personnel and public with details of site security systems.
- Details of the removal/isolation of electrical, gas and other services.
- Details of temporary services required and welfare services provided.
- Arrangements for the disposal of waste and other environmental considerations (dust, noise, pollution of water, contaminated ground).
- Details of controls covering substances hazardous to health and flammable substances, e.g. asbestos, LPG, compressed gases, and any permit-to-work system.
- Arrangements for the control and co-ordination of the site, e.g. transport, contractors, storage.
- Training requirements and competencies of personnel involved in the demolition process.
- Identification of people with special responsibilities for the co-ordination and control of safety and emergency procedures/arrangements.

Isolation or Diversion of Services

Before any work commences, all utility companies should be contacted with a request that services be disconnected or isolated. They should receive a plan of the work to be carried out.

Temporary Services

Temporary electrical systems and other temporary services should be suitable for use on the site and be robust enough to withstand the demolition conditions.

Temporary services MUST be marked so that they can all be positively identified to ensure they are not disturbed, damaged or removed. They should undergo regular visual examination and test by a competent person.

Soft-Strip Requirements

Soft-strip allows a planned progressive removal of products and services from the structure causing as little damage as possible to the infrastructure. Often, items removed are stripped and packed away for re-use.

Working at Height

Means of access for work at height will have to be means that can be extended or reduced as the work progresses.

Scaffolding must be of a suitable type - often tied scaffold is not suitable on buildings that are being demolished, or cannot be used due to dilapidation or incomplete structures; portable units may be more appropriate.

Protection of the Public and Others

Potential hazards should be isolated; this also helps to exclude persons from the site who are not directly involved.

- A fence (>2m) should be erected enclosing all the demolition operations. It should not be capable of being easily climbed.
- Access gates should be secured outside working hours.
- Danger notices should be displayed.
- Where perimeter fencing is not practicable, excavations should be fenced.
- Lighting may be required in high-risk areas.
- Debris fans and facade netting may be required to prevent people being accidentally struck by falling objects. These must be cleared of debris regularly, and checked for damage.
- Any ladders in use must be regularly checked to ensure they remain tied after each time they are moved.

Emergency Arrangements

- **Need for Emergency Preparedness**

  All organisations need procedures in place to cope with emergencies of different forms and scales. Typical emergency procedures that a demolition contractor might need to consider include: chemical spillage or gas/vapour release, fire evacuation, first-aid treatment, bomb threat and major incident.

  The requirement for emergency planning is included in many pieces of health and safety legislation (either expressly or implied) including the **MHSWR 1999**, **COSHH 2002** and **DSEAR 2002**.

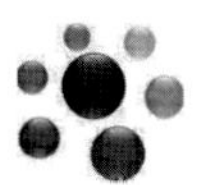

- **Development of Emergency Plans**

  The contractor or principal contractor must prepare and provide a current Emergency Contacts Set of Procedures for each work site. They should be followed in any site emergency and contain emergency telephone numbers and methods of notifying services.

  The emergency plan document is formal and written. It is designed to assist management with the control of specific hazards or incidents, so that minimum disruption to normal work occurs.

  All potential major disruptive circumstances need to be identified, individual emergency plans must then be drawn up.

  For a plan to operate efficiently, responsibilities must be set down and understood. It will include non-company personnel, as external services may be involved in both development and implementation.

  Someone within the company (e.g. the Safety Officer for the contractor) should be trained to deal with the media. The role can have a profound effect on company image.

Separation and Disposal of Waste

Waste includes any substance or object to be discarded or recycled:

- **Solid waste** should be stored or isolated and labelled correctly to be disposed of by licensed contractors in accordance with the **Duty of Care** under the **Environmental Protection Act 1990 Part II** and associated regulations. Materials and containers with hazardous properties (e.g. oil, diesel, asbestos) may need to be dealt with as 'hazardous waste'.
- **Liquid waste** should be clearly labelled, stored and contained in a bunded area to prevent contamination to be subsequently disposed of using a permitted facility. Liquid wastes and effluents cannot be discharged into the sewer system or watercourse without prior written authorisation.

Competence of Workforce

Workers must have necessary levels of competence and health and safety training. In the case of a subcontractor, the presence of a health and safety policy, the suitability of method statements, previous work and accident history, quality of risk assessments and the level of training of staff would be a guide to such competence.

Communications

Good communications must remain in place throughout the demolition project. The method statement should show what internal means of communication are available, and how regular communication will be achieved. Essential external contacts will also be maintained.

Asbestos

Before work starts, the owner or controller of the site must provide an asbestos management plan. It will detail the steps to avoid exposure to asbestos, and where it cannot be totally avoided, how co-ordination with licensed asbestos removal contractors (where necessary) will take place. Control of waste and disposal will be detailed.

Control Measures for Identified Hazards

Where hazards are identified in the risk assessment, the control measures will be detailed in the method statement, together with notification of who is responsible for ensuring they are put in place and followed.

Plant and Equipment

All plant and equipment will be indicated, together with details of authorised and competent operators.

Access and Egress from Site

Vehicle and pedestrian access routes must be under constant review.

Where scaffolding is used, platforms and gangways must be kept free from debris and tripping hazards. The security of scaffolds is important and monitoring is required to see that when the structure is demolished sufficient ties are maintained with the building.

Some operations require the demolition worker to occupy precarious positions where it is not possible to provide an adequate safety structure. Here safety harnesses should be used and attached to a secure part of the structure. Where floors have been removed, some boards should be left so there remains a skeleton floor structure to allow work to proceed in relative safety.

Training and Welfare Arrangements

- **Training**

  The foreman/supervisor is the key competent person in demolition projects. The supervisor must be in constant attendance where there is danger of a sudden collapse. In some more complex cases it may be necessary to seek advice from a qualified engineer.

  Training should be secured from nationally accredited bodies such as CITB and the National Demolition Training Group. Written records should be kept of training received by employees. Demolition training should comply with recommendations contained in **BS 6187:2000 British Standard Code of Practice for Demolition**.

  More specialised training may be necessary in relation to work involving some unusual or special hazards.

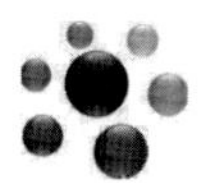

- **Welfare Facilities**

  The basic requirements are for washing, toilet, rest and changing facilities and drying rooms, as well as somewhere clean to eat and drink during meal breaks with drinking water. The basic requirement may sometimes go beyond this to the provision of showers if risk assessment requires it.

  Changing facilities may be needed if work clothes are too dirty or contaminated to travel home in. If site-specific clothing might contaminate other clothing, then it should be stored separately.

Named Responsible Persons

All construction and demolition activities are covered by the **CDM Regulations 2015**. This places duties on:

- **The client** - to make suitable arrangements for managing a project, including the allocation of sufficient time and other resources, and ensure that these arrangements are maintained and reviewed throughout the project.
- **The contractor** - to plan, manage and monitor the demolition activity and co-ordinate matters relating to health and safety to ensure that the work is carried out without risks to health or safety.

Co-ordination of Activities On Site

Demolition work requires a more rigorous approach to co-ordination, co-operation and planning than general construction. Those undertaking the work need to understand the risks and any appropriate action required. A written demolition plan is important for high-risk work.

The demolition plan must be prepared by those in control before work starts and will detail arrangements of how the work will be carried out.

The principal contractor prepares and reviews the demolition plan that identifies safety risks and the measures to address them. He/she also co-ordinates the activities of all contractors to ensure compliance with both legislation and the demolition plan. Consequently, the principal contractor may give information, instruction and site induction to other contractors and arrange for their training.

Exam-Style Questions

Short Questions

1. **Outline** the principal topics to be dealt with in a demolition method statement.
(8 marks)

2. A four-storey building is to be demolished.

   Outline the environmental hazards that are likely to be caused by the work and, for **EACH**, **outline** the actions necessary to eliminate or control them.
(8 marks)

3. A demolition contractor has been engaged to demolish a disused chemical factory.

   Outline the preparatory information that the factory owner should supply to the contractor in a pre-demolition survey. (8 marks)

4. A 1960s-built multi-storey car park in a city centre location is to be demolished and cleared as part of a major redevelopment programme.
   (a) **Outline** the foreseeable hazards, associated with the demolition project, that could affect members of the general public. (4 marks)
   (b) **Outline** how the hazards identified in (a) should be managed so that risk is prevented or controlled. (4 marks)

(Total: 8 marks)

Long Question

5. The owners of a large industrial site are to have the buildings on the site demolished before selling the site for redevelopment.

   Outline all of the main issues that the principal contractor should address in the health and safety plan for the management of the demolition project.
(20 marks)

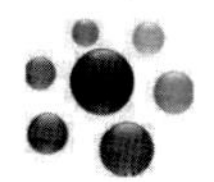

Model Answers

Short Questions

1. The demolition method statement should generally set out the sequence of work and the methods for each part:

   - Preparation work (pre-weakening, temporary propping, isolation of existing services).
   - Dealing with hazardous materials.
   - The provision of temporary services.
   - Emergency procedures.
   - Control and co-ordination on site.
   - Competency of workers.

2. The likely environmental hazards would be:

   - Noise.
   - Dust.
   - Silt, affecting drainage systems.
   - Mud and debris on adjacent roads.

   The corresponding control actions would be:

   - Damping down the structure to reduce the production of dust.
   - Sheeting up of disposal vehicles.
   - Noise controls such as barriers.
   - Fitting filters or stoppers to site drainage gullies.
   - Bunding of fuel tanks.

3. Preparatory information that the factory owner should provide includes:
   - Location of site services (including buried services).
   - Hazardous/flammable substances stored on site.
   - Location of dangerous machinery.
   - Details of factory structure (also any known weaknesses).
   - Means of access.
   - Details of traffic routes.
   - Proximity of neighbours.

4. (a) Hazards likely to affect the general public; four from the following:
   - Premature collapse of the structure affecting both pedestrians and passing traffic.
   - Materials falling onto pavements and pedestrian areas.
   - Mud being carried onto the surrounding roadways.
   - Dust and fumes escaping from the area during general demolition work.
   - Noise from the use of plant and equipment being used.
   - Hazardous substances being released: asbestos, PCBs, lead fume from lead paint, flammable liquids on site releasing vapours.

   (b) The hazards should be managed in the following ways:
   - Prevention of premature collapse of the structure with the use of propping and shoring systems.
   - Prevention of materials falling on passers-by by use of gantries, fans, crash decks and sheeting.
   - Carriage of mud could be prevented by vehicle wheel washing and possible mechanical road-sweeping around the site exits.
   - Dust and fume could be prevented by applying a COSHH assessment, using low dust-emitting techniques of demolition, using water sprays to damp down dust and covering wagons and skips.
   - Noise reduction techniques should be used following a noise assessment; use equipment with low operating noise levels, use solid-panelled fencing around the site, restrict hours of demolition to prevent noise nuisance during night-time hours.
   - Hazardous substance emission, particularly asbestos and lead fumes, should be eliminated completely by prior stripping of the building following a survey by a competent person prior to main demolition works.

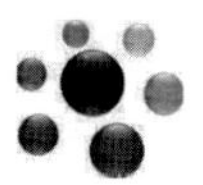

Long Question

5. The main issues to be addressed as part of the health and safety plan:

   - Arrangements to co-ordinate all contractors on site.
   - Risk assessment (including COSHH and noise assessments).
   - The sequence of work.
   - The demolition method statement.
   - Procedures for evaluating competency of sub-contractors.
   - Arrangements for liaising with client, principal designer and principal contractor.

   The main issues connected directly with work:

   - The control of noise and dust (particularly asbestos).
   - Prevention of water course contamination.
   - Isolation of existing services.
   - Introduction of a permit-to-work system.
   - Use of plant and access equipment.
   - Traffic management systems including pedestrian segregation.
   - Access to and egress from the site.
   - Control and disposal of waste.
   - Welfare and first-aid.
   - Accident reporting procedures to HSE.
   - Provision of information.
   - Provision of training.
   - Arrangements for regular monitoring of compliance with health and safety standards.
   - Procedures on site.

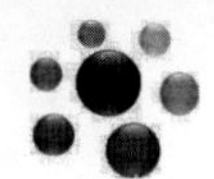

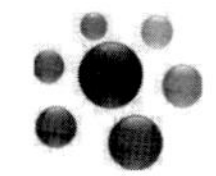

Introduction to Unit NCC2: Construction Practical Application

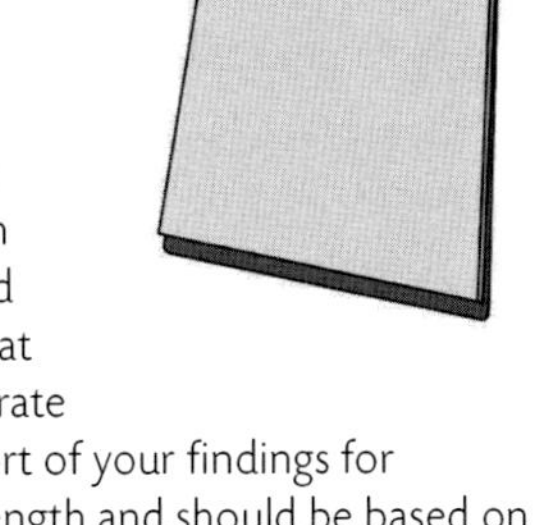

The second section of your Revision Guide will focus on what's required for the Construction Practical Application and the steps you need to take to ensure success.

This assessment is your chance to prove you understand the content from Units NCC1 and NCC2 and can apply it in a practical workplace environment. You will carry out an inspection of your chosen workplace, spotting hazards and completing the inspection record sheets. It's important that you choose a workplace with enough hazards to demonstrate the breadth of your knowledge. You will then write a report of your findings for management; this should be around 700-1000 words in length and should be based on the information in your inspection record sheets.

Preparing Effectively

Introduction

This section of the Revision Guide will help you to understand the form of the Construction Health and Safety Practical Application and how to prepare for and do well in this assessment.

There are other sources of information available on the NCC2 Practical Application. NEBOSH publish guidance on the Practical Application on their website (www.nebosh.org.uk), including a marking scheme for the assessment. If you haven't already downloaded a copy of this guidance, we strongly advise you to do so. Course providers also publish information and guidance on the NCC2 Practical Application.

This Revision Guide doesn't replicate these other sources of guidance; it is actually intended to complement them and give detailed practical guidance and advice on completing the assessment. We recommend that you check all of your course materials for any other sources of information that might supplement this revision aid.

A Note from The Author

Students taking the NEBOSH Construction Certificate qualification are often very concerned about the assessments that they have to pass at the end of the whole study process.

NEBOSH qualifications are not easy to achieve and each person who passes a qualification does so on their own merits. In some ways this should be very rewarding and reassuring. It represents one of the times in life when there are no shortcuts.

But, when you are preparing for the end of course assessments, revision and preparation can take up so much of your time and exam nerves can take over.

Students often spend a lot of time and effort preparing for the two written exams. This is only natural as these two written exams are the harder elements of the assessment process (at least this is what the national pass rates show). Unfortunately, in their efforts to do well in the written exams, students often push the practical assessment to the back of their thoughts. This can mean that students are poorly prepared to undertake the practical assessment. In some cases students fail to achieve the 60% minimum pass mark required by NEBOSH for the Practical Application. This is a great shame as a little preparation can ensure a good performance in this part of the assessment process.

The Practical Application is not easy! You can't assume that you will get a pass without putting in the effort, but with a little preparation and thought there is no reason why you shouldn't do well in it. The following guidance sets out practical guidelines and hints and tips that I have picked up over the last 12 years of teaching on NEBOSH Certificate courses. I hope that you find it useful!

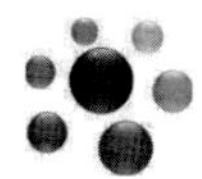

The Practical Application

An Overview of What Will Happen

There are two parts to the Practical Application:

- Carry out an unaided inspection of a workplace.
- Write a management report on your findings.

The Inspection

You will need:

A watch.

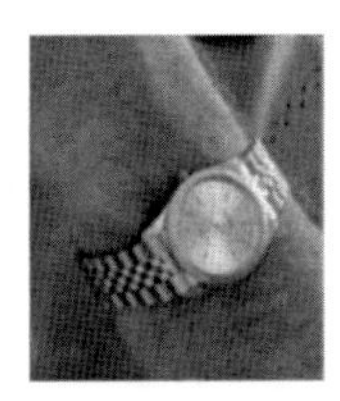

A clipboard.

A pen.

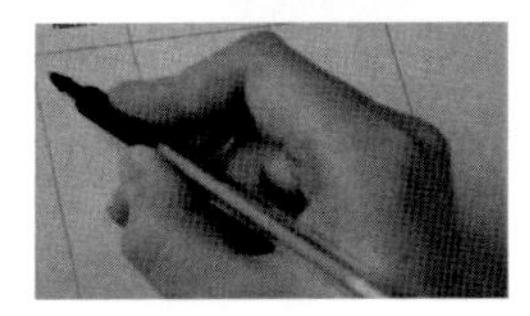

A set of blank NEBOSH Practical Application candidate's observation sheets.

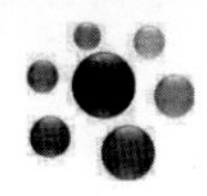

You should already have arranged a suitable construction site in which to carry out an inspection. You need to ensure that your site is large enough to provide a sufficient range of hazards but not so large that you cannot cover everything in the hour or so you have to complete your observations. If your site is very large, you should think about limiting your inspection area.

You should have a clipboard and pen and a set of NEBOSH Practical Application blank observation sheets. When the assessment starts you can walk around the workplace jotting down observations on your blank pro-forma record sheets. You may talk to workers in the workplace but remember that this is an assessment so if any of your colleagues are taking the assessment at the same time, you must not talk to them.

Once you have finished your observations, you should move to a quiet location for the second part of the assessment process.

The Management Report

You will need:

- Your completed inspection record sheets.
- Your course notes and/or reference books to refer to when writing your report.

You can choose whether to write the report up in your own handwriting or in word-processed form.

You should aim to complete the management report in around one hour and it should be around 700-1000 words in length.

Your completed observation forms should be your main source of reference but you're also able to refer to your course notes and reference books as you complete your report (but remember that plagiarism will be treated as malpractice). Your report should **not** include any photographs, printed text or extraneous material.

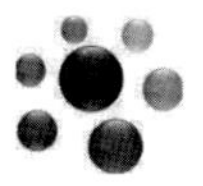

The Inspection

What to Do

Before you start your assessment, read through any resources that you have that might provide information on the practical assessment. NEBOSH publish information on the practical assessment, including the marking scheme, in their syllabus guide. If you have not already done so, you should consider buying this syllabus guide from NEBOSH. Your course materials may also provide additional guidance.

When you begin your inspection, decide how much time you intend to spend in each part of the workplace to be inspected. You must ensure that you manage your time effectively so that you inspect all of the workplace available to you - otherwise you may miss parts of the workplace where significant observations might be made.

At the start of your inspection simply stand back and observe. Don't rush to start and focus too narrowly on one issue. Take in as much of the workplace as you can. Use all of your senses. Consider the workplace environment; temperature, light, noise, etc. Consider the welfare provision. Consider the activities that you can see (if any). Consider the traffic and pedestrian routes and escape routes.

When you start to walk around the workplace making your observations, make sure that you write a full and complete set of notes on the observation sheets.

There are two possible ways of recording your observation on the inspection record sheets as you walk around:

- One option is to label separate sheets with different topic headings and then to flick to the relevant headed sheet for each observation as it is made, i.e. label the inspection sheets with topic headings such as "Fire Safety", "Electrical Safety", "Chemical Safety", "Environmental and Welfare", etc., and then write each observation on the appropriately labelled page.
- The other option is simply to write observations on the inspection record sheet as they come to hand.

And make sure that your handwriting is legible! Your observation sheets will be submitted together with your management report. If an examiner can't read your work then they can't mark your work.

As you walk around make sure that you consider a broad range of health and safety topics. Do not focus too narrowly on just one or two safety topics. You will need to consider topics such as fire safety, chemical safety, machinery safety, welfare issues, environmental issues, electrical safety, mechanical handling, people movement, vehicle movement, first-aid, PPE, ergonomics (especially with regards to DSE), work at height, noise, vibration, radiation hazards, etc. You might not spot hazards across this entire range, but you should have a good spread from many of these topic areas by the end of your inspection.

Remember that in order to identify hazards you may need to look under, behind, inside and on top of objects and equipment in the workplace.

Don't expose yourself to danger. If you don't know whether something is safe, then leave it alone. Stay alert to the fact that you are in a real workplace. NEBOSH recommend that you consult with the management of the workplace to ensure you can carry out the assessment without endangering yourself.

What to Write

The observation sheets should be completed by:

- **Identifying**, in the left-hand column, any hazards, unsafe work practices and examples of good practice observed during the inspection
- **Commenting** in the next column,on the adequacy of existing controls and identifying any immediate, medium-term and long-term remedial actions needed.
- **Stating**, in the right-hand column a reasonable timescale for the actions identified.

Observations

In the first column of the candidate's observation sheet (entitled "Observations - Hazards and Consequences") you should write a brief note on one hazard that you have observed in the workplace and its consequences. The hazard needs to be described in enough detail so that the examiner can understand what you observed, where it was and what type of risk it created. So instead of simply writing "trip hazard" write "trailing electrical flex to inside of main entrance - significant trip hazard". Then the reader can fully appreciate what you observed, where it was and what you are worried about.

Remember that a hazard is something with the potential to cause harm. It does not need to be a poorly controlled hazard. It is quite acceptable (and indeed expected) that you will make some observations about hazards that are well controlled. The majority of your observations should be on hazards that are poorly controlled.

The sorts of issues that you might make observations on in this column might include (but would not be restricted to) inadequate lighting creating a trip hazard; poor ventilation causing a health risk; manual handling of loads creating a risk of muscle strains; inadequate welfare facilities (e.g. unsanitary WCs, no access to drinking water, no rest areas) inadequate first-aid provision (e.g. poorly stocked first-aid boxes, contaminated eye wash bottles); inadequate fire precautions (e.g. no fire extinguishers, blocked escape routes); poor storage of materials (e.g. flammable gases or liquids left in inappropriate places, chemicals in unlabelled containers or unstable stacks of bricks); no traffic management; guards missing from machinery; incomplete scaffolds, ladders not tied, a failure of workers to wear appropriate PPE; etc.

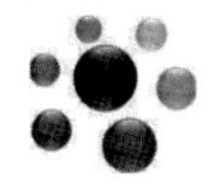

Below are five examples of observations.

Observation **Hazards and Consequences**
1. Timber off-cuts left on the ground by the main ground floor entrance.
2. Access ladder to scaffold first lift not tied.
3. Electric drill used by a plumber had a damaged cable with the inner wires showing and no evidence of PAT.
4. Old 5L oil can containing petrol being used as fuel for the cement mixer.
5. Site not secure against unauthorised access. Several Heras fence panels on south side have large gaps between them. Easy access to trespassers, especially children.

You should write at least twenty separate observations. A good target to aim for might be twenty-five observations made up of twenty negatives and five positives. Or perhaps thirty observations made up of twenty-four negatives and six positives. Do not be too concerned about precise numbers given here, consider the general principle. Do not write an excessive number of observations. Thirty should be quite enough to score well.

If you are making too many observations then you are probably repeating a lot of your hazards, e.g. making a lot of comments about poor housekeeping when one or two comments would suffice. If you are making too many observations then you are probably not writing sufficient detail on each observation as you walk around. It is the quality of your observations that is assessed here, not the quantity. Thirty detailed observations are much better than fifty one-line scribbles. You should pace yourself accordingly. If you have written ten observations in the first five minutes then you are going too fast.

Number each observation on your inspection record sheets. That way you can refer back to each item easily when you are writing your management report.

Control Measures

For every observation that you make you must complete the "Control Measures" column. As a minimum you must indicate one action that is appropriate for the observation. Most observations will have more than one appropriate action; there will be a short tem action to make the workplace safe and then there will be one or more longer term actions to keep it safe and sort out the underlying cause of the problem.

For example, if you found an untied ladder, the immediate actions will be to have the ladder tied. But that does not prevent the problem happening again. A longer-term action might therefore be to give site operatives a tool box talk on ladder safety and perhaps to introduce a routine inspection regime so that any non-compliance might be identified and stamped out quickly. You do not need to spell this out in such a lengthy manner, but you do need to identify the actions, such as "Tie ladder; Include ladders in tool box talks; Instruct site supervisor to monitor compliance".

Many observations will have a short-term safety action, a medium-term remedial action and a long-term solution.

If your observation is a positive one it is still appropriate to make a comment in this action column such as "monitor" or "ensure this good standard is maintained".

Your actions must be practical and realistic. Inappropriate actions will not win you points. If your recommendation does not solve the problem then it is not appropriate. PAT testing the cable that is trailing across the walkway does not address the trip hazard. If your recommendation is excessively costly or difficult in proportion to the risk then it is not reasonably practicable. Avoiding work at height when carrying out roof repairs is not realistic.

Timescale

For every action that you recommend you must complete the "Timescale" column. Indicate whether an action needs to be carried out immediately, within 24 hours, 2 days, 1 week, 3 months, etc. You can recommend any timescale that you feel is appropriate. Do not write "ASAP" - that is not a timescale. Do not write "Immediate" for every action - that is unrealistic. Make sure that your timescales match your actions and that they match the observation. The trailing cable in the thoroughfare must be moved immediately. The ladder tool box talk must be done within 1 week. The PAT regime introduced within 2 months. These are all appropriate.

Some of your recommended actions will be "ongoing". If your recommendation is to monitor the situation then this is an appropriate comment to make.

On the following page are five examples of recommended actions and timescales appropriate to the issues used as examples previously.

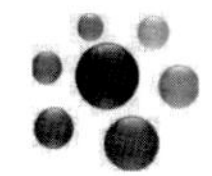

Observations Hazards and Consequences	**Control Measures Immediate and Longer-Term Actions**	**Timescale**
1. Timber off-cuts left on the ground by the main ground floor entrance. Risk of slips, trips and falls.	Clean up the area. Site foreman to monitor.	1 day Ongoing
2. Access ladder to scaffold first lift not tied. Risk of persons falling.	Tie ladder. Include ladders in tool box talks. Instruct site supervisors to monitor compliance.	Immediate 1 week Ongoing
3. Electric drill used by a plumber had a damaged cable with the inner wires showing and no evidence of PAT. Risk of electric shock.	Cease using drill until cable is repaired/replaced. Introduce PAT regime.	Immediate 2 months
4. Old 5L oil can containing petrol being used as fuel for the cement mixer. Risk of leakage and fire.	Obtain an approved container and dispose of old container safely. Site foreman to monitor.	1 day Ongoing
5. Site not secure against unauthorised access. Several Heras fence panels on south side have large gaps between them. Risk to trespassers, especially children.	Re-fix fence panels. Visual inspection of fence at the end of each day.	Before end of day Daily

Scoring High Marks

Almost a third of the Practical Application marks are available for completing these observation sheets; 30% in total. So it's worth doing a good job here and writing a decent set of comments.

The marking scheme clearly indicates where the marks are going. This marking scheme is presented in the NEBOSH syllabus guide. If you do not already have a copy of this syllabus guide then you should consider buying it.

To highlight the key points:

- **Range and number of hazards/good practice - 15%**

  If you only identify a few of the various hazards that were present in the workplace then the examiner cannot award you good marks under this section. But if you present at least twenty poorly-controlled hazards and identify some well-controlled hazards as well then you stand a good chance of picking up these marks. Do not be overly concerned with technical hazards. There will be plenty of observations to make.

  If you talk about fire safety, fire safety and more fire safety you will score 0 or 1 point under this section heading. But if your observations are across a range of relevant health and safety issues such as machinery safety, chemical safety, fire safety, noise, work at height, pedestrian movement, vehicle movements, welfare issues, working environment issues, etc. then you will score the marks here.

- **Identification of suitable control measures and timescales - 15%**

  To score well in this section you must clearly identify the immediate, medium-term and longer-term action that must be taken to resolve each of the problems you have identified. The immediate solution must make the workplace safe. The medium-term action must keep it safe and the longer-term action must fix the cause of the problem or at least be likely to stop it happening again. And all of these recommendations must be practical and realistic.

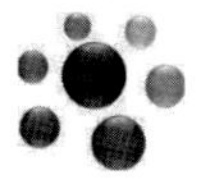

The Management Report

What to Do

Before you start your practical application, you should read through any resources that you have that might provide information on the assessment. NEBOSH publish information on the practical application, including the marking scheme, in their syllabus guide. If you have not already done so, you should consider buying this syllabus guide from NEBOSH. Your course materials may also provide additional guidance.

Look through all of the inspection record sheets that you have written and pick out a selection of the bigger issues that you intend to write about in your management report. You do not need to pick out more than five or six issues. You can make notes on a sheet of A4 to assist in this planning process.

Prioritise the issues that you intend to write about in the report so that you have the highest priority issue at the top of your list and the lowest priority issue at the bottom.

Draw up a short outline plan for your management report so that you have a rough idea of what you will include under each of the section headings.

Start your management report.

Write each of the sections of the management report. As you write each section make sure that you go back to your outline plan to ensure that you are staying on track. Tick each section off your plan as it is achieved.

If you choose to hand-write the report, make sure that your handwriting is legible. If an examiner cannot read your work then they cannot mark your work.

What to Write

Your management report must look like a management report. It must therefore be formatted in an appropriate style.

You should give your report a title. For example:

Report on Health and Safety Inspection of Barn Conversion at Ambridge Farm

Underline this title to make it obvious. This title should appear at the top of the first page of the report.

Your report must be broken up into a series of sections, as dictated by NEBOSH. Each section should have its own section title:

Introduction including overview of area inspected and activities taking place

Executive summary

Main findings of the inspection

Conclusions

Recommendations

You can number each section for presentation purposes; e.g. 1.0 Introduction; 2.0 Executive Summary; 3.0 Main Findings; 4.0 Conclusions.

Your Introduction can be quite short. It should briefly state what the report is about, when it was written, why it was written and who it was written by. This Introduction should be presented as a paragraph of text made up of just two or three sentences.

For example:

1.0 Introduction

This report follows a health and safety inspection of the barn conversion at Ambridge Farm carried out by J. Bloggs at 9:30am on 25 April 2009. The project is a luxury conversion for single residential occupation by Bodge and Co, a small local builder directly employing 10 plus various trade sub contractors. The project involves re-roofing the existing structure and insertion of a second floor together with associated ground works and internal fixes. The barn stands in its own grounds separate from the remaining farm buildings. Work started about 5 weeks ago with the old roof now removed and in the final stages of replacement while internal new floor/ partitions commenced. The purpose of the report is to bring to management's attention the key health, safety and welfare issues of concern on the site together with recommendations for improvement.

In the Executive Summary you might summarise the key areas of concern that are going to be addressed by the report. You might want to make some general comments about health and safety standards in the workplace. You should also make reference to the fact that the management report is not a comprehensive report on all of the issues that were identified by the inspection, but instead selectively picks out key issues of concern. You could also draw attention to the inspection record sheets (which are attached to the report as an appendix) as these will include all of the issues identified in the inspection, not just the ones written up in your report.

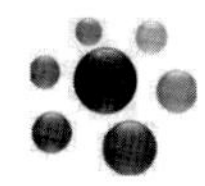

This Executive Summary might be presented as a couple of paragraphs, each made up of several sentences. Your key areas of concern might be presented as a bullet point list in order of priority.

For example:

2.0 Executive Summary

Overall, the site is tidy and provision of welfare facilities are good. There are some examples of good health and safety standards in place. However, there are also some major areas of concern. These largely arise from unsafe practices being carried out by site operatives.

This report focuses specifically on four main issues identified during the site inspection:

- Use of unguarded machinery.
- Site security.
- Electrical safety.
- Non-compliance with Personal Protective Equipment (PPE) rules.

Many other issues were identified during the inspection that also require attention. These observations, along with their corrective actions, are attached to this report as an appendix.

Your Main Findings section is likely to be further sub-divided into sections on each of the key findings that you want to discuss. It makes sense, therefore, to split your main findings up into a series of sub-sections, each with their own sub-section title. If you have used section numbers then you should number these subsections: 3.1, 3.2, 3.3, etc.

Your Main Findings section is where you should selectively discuss the major issues that you want to bring to the manager's attention. It is not for trivia. It is not for a complete repetition of all of the issues identified during the inspection. You must therefore select a number of key topics to discuss in this section. You might do this by picking out just one of the issues from your inspection sheets that is quite major in its own right. Or you might pick out a series of observations which is not a big issue when they're looked at individually, but all together add up to an important issue. For example, if you saw one worker using a piece of industrial machinery without the correct guards in place you would be quite right in identifying that one breach as an important issue that is worth discussing in the management report. If you saw one site operative not wearing a hard hat, that would not be a significant enough issue to mention in the report.

However, if you saw six site operatives not complying with the site rules on PPE then you would be quite entitled to combine these under the title of 'Personal Protective Equipment' for discussion as one of the key findings in your report.

When discussing your main findings it is quite acceptable to refer to the inspection sheets and quite acceptable to refer to specific issues by making use of the relevant reference numbers. For example, "I observed six significant PPE safety issues during the inspection (see items 6, 14 and 22 on the inspection sheets)."

For each of the key findings of your report you should write several short paragraphs under a sub-section title. Under each sub-section title you should describe the nature of the issue found during the inspection; the particular legal standards relevant to the issue; the action or actions that you believe are appropriate; the costs associated with these actions; some justification as to why these costs are worth incurring. In short: this is the problem, this is the relevant law, this is what you need to do about it, this is how much it will cost you, this is why you want to spend that money.

For example:

3.0 Main Findings

The site was generally tidy with exemplary washing, toilet and rest room facilities.

3.1 Use of Unguarded Machinery

During my inspection I observed one worker on site using a hand held circular saw. There was no guard fitted to the blade of the circular saw. The blade was exposed for its entire circumference. This presents a high risk of severe injury including amputation of body parts and even fatal lacerations. This also represents a clear breach of the Provision and Use of Work Equipment Regulations 1998 (PUWER).

I recommend that this piece of machinery be taken out of use with immediate effect. The guards must be reinstated on this machine before it is put back into use. If no guards can be found then this piece of equipment must be disposed of in such a way that it cannot be put back into use. Total cost of these actions will be negligible. Should a new item of equipment have to be purchased then this will cost in the range of £100.

To prevent this situation from arising again I also recommend that a series of toolbox talks or briefings to workers are carried out on the safe use of this type of equipment and other similar tools. These briefings should be formally recorded. These briefings can be resourced

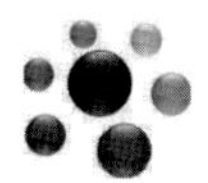

and provided internally at the cost of perhaps half a day's labour for one site supervisor.

I would further recommend that the site supervisors are given a written memo about the importance of maintaining vigilance and challenging unsafe acts when they see them. This may have been a one-off matter, but it may indicate a more deep-rooted apathy to safety management by site staff. Needless to say, if an enforcement officer had observed this unsafe practice they would have issued a prohibition notice on the spot and they might well have considered prosecuting the company, site managers and the worker himself.

3.2 Site Security

3.3 Electrical safety

3.4 Non-compliance with PPE Rules

3.5 Unsafe Storage of Flammable Liquids...

You should write about a minimum of three main findings, i.e. there should be at least three sub-sections under your main findings title. You might write about four main issues. You might write about five. It is probably not sensible to include more than six. Four is quite acceptable.

Your Conclusions section should complete your report. You should make reference to the general standards of health and safety found in the workplace and the specific issues of concern. You should summarise the recommendations made and the key reasons for the manager to act on these recommendations.

For example:

4.0 Conclusions

Overall, this is a well run, tidy site and the welfare facilities were exemplary. There are, however, a number of important health and safety failings that do require your urgent attention:

- Use of unguarded machinery.
- Site security.
- Electrical safety.
- Non-compliance with Personal Protective Equipment (PPE) rules.
- Unsafe storage of flammable liquids.

Each of these issues represents a breach of health and safety regulations and a possible breach of the Health and Safety at Work Act 1974. As such they might incur enforcement action from an HSE inspector in the form of Improvement or Prohibition Notices. They might even result in prosecution of the company under the Act, which could result in a fine. Needless to say, the adverse publicity and damage done to the company's reputation might be severe and could make a difference to its financial success. Workforce morale will also be lowered with a likely adverse effect on quality of work and productivity. I should mention the costs of any compensation claims for injury which will likely result in increased insurance costs. The moral dimension is also important as you and the victims of preventable injury will have to live with the consequences.

Please note that other issues not discussed in the report do require action and these have been included in the full set of candidate's observation sheets attached to this report.

You should complete your report by summarising the recommendations made and the key reasons for the manager to act on these recommendations. Your recommendations must appear in the form of a table laid down by NEBOSH:

Recommendation	Likely Resource Implications	Priority	Target Date

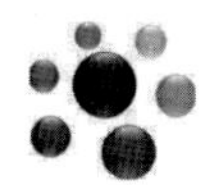

An example might be:

5.0 Recommendations

Recommendation	**Likely Resource Implications**	**Priority**	**Target Date**
Hand-held circular saw should be taken out of use with immediate effect. The guards must be reinstated on this machine before it is put back into use (or the machine disposed of if the guards cannot be located).	Negligible. Should a new saw have to be purchased, this will cost in the range of £100.	Immediate	48 hours
Hold a series of toolbox talks on the safe use of saws and other similar tools.	These can be run internally at the cost of perhaps half a day's labour for one site supervisor.	High	1 week
Provide site supervisors with a written memo about the importance of maintaining vigilance and challenging unsafe acts when they see them.	Developed internally at the cost of half an hour's labour for one site supervisor.	High	1 Week

Issue of PPE to employees should be reviewed to ensure all have personal issue of (or access to) the PPE stipulated in the site rules.	Less than 1 hour of site foreman's time. Minimal overhead of around £30 per employee to rectify shortfalls.	Medium	2 weeks
Check that contractual arrangements with sub-contractors include site rules on PPE.	A few minutes of Contract Director's time to check. Up to 2 hour's time if arrangements are not already in place.	Medium	2 weeks
Ongoing site monitoring of compliance by site foreman and all Directors.	No specific costs or additional time required.		

Your management report must be written using appropriate language. Avoid the use of slang. Avoid sweeping generalisations. Avoid repetition.

Your management report must hit the right tone. It must be short, concise and supported by reasoned arguments. It must not be strident, heavily opinionated or biased. It is not an enforcement order. It must not be long, unfocused, rambling and dull. If a real manager were to read it in a real workplace they should find the report compelling. One way to hit the right tone is to think of yourself as the company Safety Officer. You have no authority over the manager you are writing this report for and so cannot force them to do what you are suggesting. Instead you have to persuade them by the power of your argument.

Scoring High

Just over two-thirds of the Practical Assessment marks are available for the management report - 70% in total.

The marking scheme clearly indicates where the marks are going. This marking scheme is presented in the NEBOSH syllabus guide.

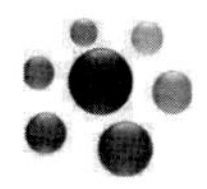

To highlight the key points:

- **Introduction providing an overview of the chosen area - 5%**

  If your introduction includes a clear and appropriate description of the chosen area and the activities taking place there, you will score well here.

- **Executive summary - 5%**

  If you provide a clear summary of the issues identified during the inspection in this section, you will score well.

- **Main Findings - Quality of interpretation of findings and clear references to strengths and weaknesses - 15%**

  In this section, you need to show a logical progression from the observation sheets to your findings. This means that you shouldn't raise any new issues in your report that have not been mentioned in your observation sheets. You need to show the examiner that you have discussed appropriately the key issues identified in your inspection and provided clear references to the strengths and weaknesses you found.

- **Main findings - Identification of possible breaches of legislation - 5%**

  Here you have to show the examiner that you can apply what you have found back to legislative requirements. To score well, you should aim to supply appropriate references to five possible breaches of legislation and demonstrate a clear understanding of the reasons for the breaches. You will not score well in this section if you provide a list of legislation with no explanation of how it was breached or how it related to the hazards, unsafe conditions or work practices selected.

  Note that you are allowed to reference your course notes and reference books when completing the report so your examiner will expect the titles and years of all legislation to be accurate!

- **Persuasiveness/conciseness/technical content - 10%**

  To score well here you need to provide clear moral, legal and financial arguments that will convince management to take action. You will also gain marks in this section for structuring your report well. You will not score well if you simply duplicate what you have written on your observation sheets!

- **Clear and concise conclusions which are clearly related to report findings and are effective in convincing management to take action - 15%**

  To score well here you need to summarise the findings you outlined in your report clearly and concisely. You will not score well here if you introduce new issues that you haven't previously discussed.

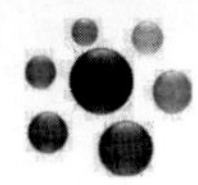

- **Recommendations which present realistic actions to improve health and safety in the chosen area - 15%**

  If your recommendations relate back to your conclusions, you will score well here. Your recommendations should be realistic and prioritised appropriately. You will also need to attempt to quantify the costs associated with most of your recommendations. Your report does not need to list the precise costs in currency terms. Simply reflecting on the approximate costs is sufficient. This might be done in terms of hours of labour, management time, or by making reference to internal and external costs.

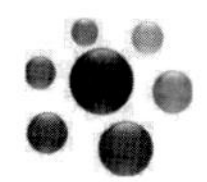

Final Reminders

Workplace Inspection	**Report to Management**
Start by taking a good look at your surroundings. Try to get a feel for the sorts of hazards and unsafe practices you should be looking for.	Keep in mind that the report to management has to successfully persuade management to take appropriate action.
Identify between 20 and 30 examples of hazards and consequences, unsafe practices and good practices and explain them in enough detail.	The report should be around 700-1000 words in length, which is equivalent to three or four sides of A4 paper.
Ensure you include hazards under a range of different topics (at least 4 or 5). Two separate examples of a trailing lead will only get you 1 mark!	The report needs to be structured appropriately with a: ■ Title ■ Introduction ■ Executive summary ■ Main Findings ■ Conclusions ■ Recommendations ■ Date and signature The report should be written in concise, formal language and be broken down into distinct sections.
Remember the definitions of high, medium and low priority and don't describe everything as high priority - you need to show you can differentiate between them.	The report should clearly identify what the main findings of the inspection were, with sufficient detail to allow the Examiner to understand what was observed, what the risks were and what breaches have occurred.
When explaining what action is required to eliminate or control each hazard or unsafe working practice, be concise but give the Examiner enough detail.	The report should clearly identify what corrective actions must be taken, with an indication of cost implications and some explanation of why this corrective action is necessary.

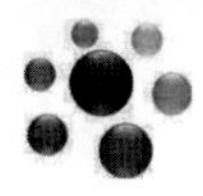

<table>
<tr>
<td>Give more than one recommended action for each hazard - an immediate action to make the hazard safe and another longer-term action that fixes the underlying problem.</td>
<td>Keep in mind the areas that the Examiner is going to be looking at when marking your report:
■ Introduction - 0-5 marks.
■ Executive summary - 0-5 marks.
■ Interpretation of findings - 0-15 marks.
■ Identification of breaches of legislation - 0-5 marks.
■ Persuasiveness/conciseness/technical content - 0-10 marks.
■ Conclusions - 0-15 marks.
■ Recommendations - 0-15 marks.
You need to score well in each of these areas to pass.</td>
</tr>
<tr>
<td>Keep in mind the areas that the Examiner is going to be looking at when marking your inspection:
■ Range and outline of hazards and consequences - 0-15 marks.
■ Identification of suitable control measures and timescales - 0-15 marks.
You need to score well in each of these areas to pass.</td>
<td></td>
</tr>
<tr>
<td colspan="2">Remember to include everything when you submit the practical assessment to us for marking, including:
■ Your completed observation sheets.
■ Your completed report (laid out in the required structure).
■ A signed declaration that the submission is your own work (remember that if this is missing, your result may be declared void!).</td>
</tr>
</table>

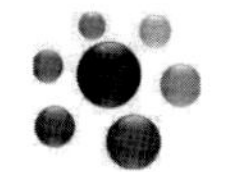

And Finally...

Hopefully, this Revision Guide has provided you with relevant practice questions and some ideas for handling them in the exam, as well as some useful guidance for tackling your NEBOSH Construction Practical Application.

It should have shown you that the exam questions are straightforward, but that it is vital that you READ THE QUESTION and answer the question that is written (not the one that you want it to be!).

It is really important to practise as many exam questions as possible - the Examiner's Reports for previous exams can be purchased from NEBOSH (0116 263 4700) or online at www.nebosh.org.uk. These Examiner's Reports don't provide model answers, but nevertheless highlight important points that should have been included in your answer.

In order to do well in the assessment, it is really important to understand what is expected of you, and one of the best ways to achieve this is to practise as much as possible. Why not take the time to do a practice inspection and report before the real assessment? You can then check your report and inspection sheets against your course materials to ensure you noted all of the hazards and gave the best possible advice in your report. You could even do a practice assessment in your own home - remember the hazards present may be well managed, but they will exist! The more familiar you are with the structure of a workplace inspection and report to management, the more comfortable you will be when your assessment date arrives.

Lastly, don't panic, but do ensure that you are prepared - you want to make sure that all your hard work will be rewarded.

Good luck!